THE ULTIMATE
CALGARY FLAMES
TRIVIA BOOK

A Collection of Amazing Trivia Quizzes and Fun Facts for Die-Hard Flames Fans!

Ray Walker

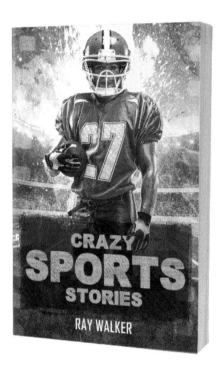

CONTENTS

INTRODUCTION

Team fandom should be inspirational. Our attachment to our favorite teams should fill us with pride, excitement, loyalty, and a sense of fulfillment in knowing that we are part of a community with many other fans who feel the same way.

Flames fans are no exception. With a rich, successful history in the NHL, the Calgary Flames have inspired their supporters to strive for greatness with their tradition of colorful players, memorable eras, big moves, and unique moments.

This book is meant to be a celebration of those moments and an examination of the collection of interesting, impressive, or important details that allow us to understand the full stories behind the players and the team.

You may use the book as you wish. Each chapter contains 20 quiz questions in a mixture of multiple-choice and true-false formats, an answer key (Don't worry, it's on a separate page!), and a section of 10 "Did You Know?" facts about the team.

Some will use it to test themselves with the quiz questions. How much Flames history do you really know? How many of the finer points can you remember? Some will use it competitively (Isn't that the heart of sports?), waging contests with friends and fellow devotees to see who can lay claim to being the biggest fan. Some will enjoy it as a learning experience, gaining insight to enrich their fandom and add color to their understanding of their favorite team. Still others may use it to teach, sharing the wonderful anecdotes inside to inspire a new generation of fans to hop aboard the Flames bandwagon.

Whatever your purpose may be, we hope you enjoy delving into the amazing background of Calgary Flames hockey!

Oh…for the record, information and statistics in this book are current up to the beginning of 2020. The Flames will surely topple more records and win more awards as the seasons pass, so keep this in mind when you're watching the next game with your friends, and someone starts a conversation with "Did you know…?".

CHAPTER 1:

ORIGINS & HISTORY

QUIZ TIME!

1. In which year did the Calgary Flames begin playing in the National Hockey League?

   a. 1972

   b. 1977

   c. 1980

   d. 1983

2. When the Flames came to Calgary, demand was so high that the team was able to sell season tickets for standing room only sections.

   a. True

   b. False

3. How was the nickname "Flames" chosen for the team?

   a. It was kept when the team moved from Atlanta, where it referenced the city's burning during the Civil War.

   b. It was adopted to contrast with the provincial rival

Edmonton Oilers so that Calgary's team would appear stronger.

c. It was voted on by fans in a media-driven "name the team" contest.

d. It was an acronym for the combined initials of the last names of the franchise owners.

4. In which season did the Flames begin to play in their new arena, the Calgary Saddledome, which was built for the 1988 Winter Olympics?

a. 1980
b. 1983
c. 1988
d. 1989

5. What is the fan base of the Calgary Flames informally known as?

a. The Fire Brigade
b. Flames Fans Forever
c. The Calgary Club
d. The C of Red

6. In which season did the Calgary Flames earn their first-ever playoff berth?

a. 1980-81
b. 1983-84
c. 1985-86
d. 1988-89

7. When Calgary's owners bought the Atlanta Flames to move them to Calgary, the price was $16 million, which was a record price for an NHL team.

    a. True

    b. False

8. How many times in their franchise history have the Flames won a division title?

    a. 2

    b. 6

    c. 8

    d. 11

9. Who was the first Flame ever to be named as Calgary's representative in the NHL All-Star Game?

    a. Guy Chouinard

    b. Doug Risebrough

    c. Pekka Rautakallio

    d. Kent Nilsson

10. Where do the Calgary Flames rank among Canadian NHL franchises in Stanley Cup championships won?

    a. 1st

    b. 3rd

    c. 5th

    d. 7th

11. How did the Flames fare during their 25th anniversary season in the NHL?

    a. Did not make the playoffs

b. Lost in the Stanley Cup Finals to the Tampa Bay Lightning

c. Did not play due to a lockout

d. Lost in the quarterfinals to the San Jose Sharks

12. The Flames' record for most goals by a player in one season was set very early in their tenure, when forward Lanny McDonald netted 66 in 1982-83.

a. True

b. False

13. Which team did Calgary face in its first-ever NHL game?

a. Edmonton Oilers

b. Toronto Maple Leafs

c. Detroit Red Wings

d. Quebec Nordiques

14. Calgary's current top farm team plays in the American Hockey League. What is this team called?

a. Abbotsford Heat

b. St. John's Flames

c. Stockton Heat

d. Seattle Inferno

15. Which player scored the first-ever goal for the Calgary Flames?

a. Dana Murzyn

b. Guy Chouinard

c. Jim Peplinski

d. Willi Plett

16. Calgary has sent more players to the Winter Olympics to represent their countries than any other NHL franchise.

    a. True
    b. False

17. Which Canadian country singer serves as the Flames' anthem singer at most home games?

    a. Reba McEntire
    b. Travis Gwillem
    c. Shania Twain
    d. George Canyon

18. Calgary was the first NHL team to introduce a mascot at its games. What is the name of this mascot?

    a. Burny the Firefighter
    b. Harvey the Hound
    c. Smokey the Bear
    d. Sparky the Flame

19. What incident is the Flames mascot most famous for?

    a. He caused a delay to the start of a game when he got tangled up while rappelling from the ceiling.
    b. He accidentally shattered a pane of glass when pretending to body check a young child into the boards.
    c. He had his tongue ripped out by an Edmonton Oilers coach.
    d. He "ice-skied" behind the team's Zamboni.

20. The Flames recorded the first outdoor game shutout in NHL history by blanking the Montreal Canadiens 4-0 at McMahon Stadium in the 2011 Heritage Classic.

    a. True
    b. False

QUIZ ANSWERS

1. C – 1980

2. A – True

3. A – It was kept when the team moved from Atlanta, where it referenced the city's burning during the Civil War.

4. B – 1983

5. D – The C of Red

6. A – 1980-81

7. A – True

8. B – 6

9. D – Kent Nilsson

10. C – 5th

11. C – Did not play due to a lockout

12. A – True

13. D – Quebec Nordiques

14. C – Stockton Heat

15. B – Guy Chouinard

16. B – False

17. D – George Canyon

18. B – Harvey the Hound

19. C – He had his tongue ripped out by an Edmonton Oilers coach.

20. A – True

DID YOU KNOW?

1. During their NHL tenure, the Calgary Flames have been shuffled around organizationally from time to time. They have played in the Patrick Division, Smythe Division, Pacific Division, and Northwest Division, and have been slotted into both the Campbell Conference and the Western Conference.

2. Professional hockey in Calgary dates back to the 1920s, when the Calgary Tigers roamed the ice (and, in an interesting case of foreshadowing, lost the Stanley Cup to the Montreal Canadiens). When the Tigers folded in 1927, the city was left without a team until the Calgary Cowboys joined the WHA in 1975. The Cowboys lasted just two years, but luckily, the Flames relocated to town shortly afterward.

3. The Scotiabank (formerly Olympic) Saddledome has been home to the Flames for most of their existence. The building features a unique curved roof in the shape of a saddle, nodding to the area's cowboy and ranching traditions. It once appeared on the cover of *Time* magazine.

4. The Flames have shared the Saddledome with a few other tenants. The Calgary 88's of the World Basketball League played there, as did the Calgary Rad'z of Roller Hockey International and the Calgary Outlaws of the National Basketball League. Currently, the Flames share it with the

Calgary Hitmen of the Western Hockey League and the Calgary Roughnecks of the National Lacrosse League.

5. A stretch of 17ᵗʰ Avenue SW in Calgary became famous during the Flames' 2004 playoff run. Thousands of fans, mostly clad in red Flames gear, partied, watched games, and celebrated wins, leading to international media coverage of the phenomenon, which became known as "The Red Mile."

6. Calgary neither won nor lost their first NHL game at home in the Calgary Corral. The game against the Quebec Nordiques ended in a 5-5 tie. For the season, they finished with an excellent record of 25-5-10 at home.

7. Calgary's biggest NHL rival is generally thought to be the Edmonton Oilers because the two share a geographic proximity, joined the NHL and rose to power around the same time, and have an urban vs. rural divide. The Flames have the advantage in the head-to-head rivalry, but the Oilers have won more championships.

8. After moving to Calgary from Atlanta, the Flames quickly won over the fans in Alberta. For their first decade in town, the 1980s, the Flames made the playoffs every single year and advanced to the Stanley Cup Finals twice, winning it to close out the decade in 1989.

9. The 2004-05 Calgary Flames led an exciting playoff run to the Stanley Cup Finals. Before finally succumbing to the Tampa Bay Lightning, they became the first team ever to knock off three division winners along the way, beating

the Vancouver Canucks, Detroit Red Wings, and San Jose Sharks.

10. In their very first year in Calgary, the Flames not only made the playoffs but won two rounds against the Chicago Blackhawks and Philadelphia Flyers before being eliminated by the Minnesota North Stars.

CHAPTER 2:

JERSEYS & NUMBERS

QUIZ TIME!

1. When they began playing in the NHL, the Flames used what color scheme for their uniforms?

   a. Black, yellow, and orange
   b. Red and orange
   c. Black and yellow
   d. Red, white, and yellow

2. The numbers 0 and 00 have been banned from circulation by Calgary's ownership because they are seen as representing a losing attitude.

   a. True
   b. False

3. Center Mikael Backlund was given number 11 by Flames general manager Darryl Sutter and was happy to get it for all of the following reasons except which one?

   a. His wife was born on November 11.
   b. He got engaged on May 11.

c. He got married on August 11.

d. He had a child on October 11.

4. Why does center Mark Jankowski sport number 77 for the Flames?

    a. His favorite number, 14, is out of circulation because it was Theoren Fleury's, but $7 + 7 = 14$.

    b. He admired Boston Bruins Ray Bourque's class while growing up, and always wanted to wear that number.

    c. He was born in 1977.

    d. He chose it because number 7 is lucky, so this way he would have twice as much luck.

5. Aside from the standard "Flaming C" logo, what else have the Flames frequently sported on the front of their jerseys?

    a. A silhouette of a cowboy hat

    b. A patch featuring a rider on a horse

    c. A flaming horsehead crest

    d. A fireman's helmet logo

6. Five jersey numbers have proven to be most popular with the Flames, each having been worn by 23 players. Which of the following numbers is NOT one of them?

    a. 15

    b. 16

    c. 22

    d. 25

7. No Calgary Flames player ever wore number 99 before it was retired throughout the NHL in 2000.

a. True

b. False

8. Two players have worn 93, the highest-numbered jersey in Flames franchise history. Who were these two players?

    a. Michael Nylander and Doug Gilmour

    b. Alan Quine and Josh Jooris

    c. Doug Gilmour and Sam Bennett

    d. Mike Cammalleri and Sam Bennett

9. Which hockey icon did young Finnish defender Juuso Valimaki pay homage to by choosing to wear number 8 on his jersey?

    a. Teemu Selanne

    b. Alexander Ovechkin

    c. Cam Neely

    d. Mark Recchi

10. During his brief tenure in Calgary, Jaromir Jagr became the only Flame to ever wear which uniform number?

    a. 91

    b. 79

    c. 68

    d. 86

11. Joe Nieuwendyk's number 25 was retired by his alma mater, Cornell University, in 2010, joining which other hockey player's as the first retired numbers in the school's history?

    a. Adam Oates

    b. Ken Dryden

c. Jim Peplinski

d. Tony Amonte

12. Star player Jarome Iginla is the only Flame ever to have worn the number 12 on his jersey.

a. True

b. False

13. Why did Flames defenseman Mark Giordano choose to wear number 5 on the back of his jersey?

a. He respected the game of another famous defenseman who wore number 5 for the Detroit Red Wings, Nicklas Lidström.

b. As a late bloomer, it took him five years after finishing junior hockey before he made the NHL.

c. He wanted to be all about the team, and thought the number symbolized the five skaters on the ice together.

d. He has five siblings and chose the number to represent his love for each one of them.

14. How many jersey numbers have the Calgary Flames retired for their former players?

a. 1

b. 3

c. 7

d. 10

15. Which player competed for the Flames for nine seasons, the shortest tenure of anyone whose number has been retired by the franchise?

a. Al MacInnis

b. Gary Roberts

c. Joel Otto

d. Lanny McDonald

16. Fifteen players have worn the number 1 in Flames history (including their time in Atlanta), and every single one of them was a goaltender.

    a. True

    b. False

17. Lucky number 7 has been worn by 23 Flames players over the years. Which skater wore it for the longest period?

    a. T.J. Brodie

    b. Joe Mullen

    c. Chuck Kobasew

    d. Chris Clark

18. Who is the Calgary player whose number was most recently retired by the club?

    a. Lanny McDonald

    b. Jarome Iginla

    c. Mike Vernon

    d. Theoren Fleury

19. Which number did defenseman Brad Marsh, who was named the first captain in Calgary history, wear on the back of his jersey?

    a. 2

    b. 5

c. 9

d. 11

20. The first Flames player to have his number retired by the team was forward Lanny McDonald. His number 9 was raised to the rafters in 1990, the year after his retirement.

a. True

b. False

QUIZ ANSWERS

1. D – Red, white, and yellow

2. B – False

3. D – He had a child on October 11.

4. A – His favorite number, 14, is out of circulation because it was Theoren Fleury's, but $7 + 7 = 14$.

5. C – A flaming horsehead crest

6. D – 25

7. A – True

8. D – Mike Cammalleri and Sam Bennett

9. A – Teemu Selanne

10. C – 68

11. B – Ken Dryden

12. B – False

13. A – He respected the game of another famous defenseman who wore number 5 for the Detroit Red Wings, Nicklas Lidström.

14. B – 3

15. D – Lanny McDonald

16. A – True

17. A – T.J. Brodie

18. B – Jarome Iginla

19. B – 5

20. A – True

DID YOU KNOW?

1. The iconic "Flaming C" logo worn by the Calgary Flames is a nod to their franchise history. The squad originally used a "Flaming A" logo in Atlanta, but chose to honor that tradition with the appropriate alphabetic change when they relocated to Calgary. Owner Nelson Skalbania thought it was a good match for the city.

2. The highest number ever sported by a Flames goaltender is number 50, which was worn by Dany Sabourin in 2004. The number was not very lucky, however, as Sabourin lasted just four games with the Flames, failing to record a win.

3. In 2012, the Flames designed the "Forever a Flame" program, which became the highest honor the team could give a player. Neither Al MacInnis nor Joe Nieuwendyk had his number retired, but both were inducted into this club and given banners that hang in the rafters.

4. Many numbers have proven unpopular with Calgary players. The following 23 numbers have gone unused in franchise history: 69, 70, 71, 72, 73, 74, 75, 76, 78, 81, 82, 83, 84, 85, 87, 90, 91, 94, 95, 96, 97, 98, and 99.

5. Flames defender T.J. Brodie entered the NHL wearing number 66 during his first three games, but took some criticism for using the number of Penguins superstar Mario Lemieux, and switched to his more familiar number 7.

6. The fans in Calgary are so loyal to the team that they'd give up the shirts off their backs. Once during a 1999 game, winger Theo Fleury got blood on his jersey and began to head to the locker room to get a clean one. A fan threw a Flames jersey to Fleury so he could stay on for his regular shift, and Fleury wore it briefly before giving it back.

7. Superstition may have scared some Flames away from wearing the number 13. Only six players in franchise history have chosen it for themselves, but four of them defeated any potential curses and had very good careers: German Titov, Mike Cammalleri, Olli Jokinen, and Johnny Gaudreau.

8. Center Derek Ryan ended up with number 10 in Calgary after having worn 33 on a previous team. A goalie teammate posted a Twitter message offering "3 dinners, 2 dog walks, and a night of babysitting" for 33. Ryan countered with "2 dinners, 1 Whole Foods gift card, and at least 2 goals allowed in every practice" and a deal was struck.

9. Flames general manager Brian Burke could be described kindly as traditional and old-school or (by those who didn't like him) as stodgy and curmudgeonly. Burke instituted a general rule during his time with Calgary that no jersey numbers higher than 40 should be used.

10. In 2011, the Flames played in the NHL Heritage Classic and designed a special jersey for the occasion. The sweater

was a throwback to the Calgary Tigers of the 1920s and 1930s and featured a paler shade of yellow, multiple stripes across the arms, a horizontal stripe across the chest, and a white "C" logo.

CHAPTER 3:

CATCHY NICKNAMES

QUIZ TIME!

1. By which alternate franchise nickname are the Calgary Flames occasionally referred to, in reference to one of the team's third jerseys?

    a. "Demon Broncos"

    b. "Haunted Horses"

    c. "Fire Skulls"

    d. "Flaming Snot Donkeys"

2. Flames defenseman Al MacInnis was commonly called "Big Shot," not due to his attitude but because of his fearsome slapshot.

    a. True

    b. False

3. Flames tough guy Brian McGrattan went by the nickname "Big Ern" in reference to which popular actor's movie character?

    a. Jason Statham in *Crank*

    b. Matt Damon in The Bourne Identity

c. Harrison Ford in *Indiana Jones*

d. Bill Murray in *Kingpin*

4. Which three forwards played together in a combination known as "The 3M Line"?

   a. Lanny McDonald, Bob MacMillan, and Dave Moss

   b. Matt Stajan, Matthew Lombardi, and Mike Cammalleri

   c. Mikael Backlund, Michael Frolík, and Matthew Tkachuk

   d. Sergei Makarov, Joe Mullen, and Dana Murzyn

5. Which Flames skater was affectionately nicknamed "Gramps" because he looked older than he actually was?

   a. Lanny McDonald

   b. Guy Chouinard

   c. Mark Giordano

   d. Martin Gelinas

6. What was long-time Calgary leader Jim Peplinski's most common nickname?

   a. "Pepper"

   b. "The Puck Goes Inski"

   c. "Peppy Lepew"

   d. "Jimmy Pop"

7. Flames defender Zarley Zalapski was given the nickname "Snores" by teammates because of all the Z's in his name.

   a. True

   b. False

8.

9. Why was center Kent Nilsson given the nicknames "Magic Man" and "Mr. Magic" by teammates?

    a. He was an amateur magician who frequently performed card tricks on team trips.

    b. He had fantastic puck skills and could make the puck do things that other players couldn't.

    c. He was best friends with famous professional magician David Copperfield.

    d. His drink of choice was a glow in the dark concoction known as a "Magic Martini."

10. In 1983, the Flames drafted heavyweight forward Stu Grimson, who was known by what intimidating nickname?

    a. "Dr. Death"

    b. "The Grim Reaper"

    c. "Smash Face"

    d. "The Avenging Angel"

11. Why did Flames fans refer to goaltender Jamie McLennan as "Noodles"?

    a. His butterfly style of goaltending shows off legs that seem as flexible as boiled spaghetti noodles.

    b. In the team's training room hot and cold tubs, McLennan would bring his own pool noodle to support his hands while he read a book.

    c. When he broke into the league, his body was as skinny as a noodle.

    d. He preferred cooking his own pasta on the minor-league team bus rather than eating at restaurants.

12. Which Flames player was known to fans and teammates by the nickname "Iggy"?

    a. Alex Tanguay

    b. Jarome Iginla

    c. Guy Chouinard

    d. Martin Gelinas

13. Winger Lanny McDonald was such a good scorer that he earned the nickname "Machine Gun Lanny" while playing junior hockey.

    a. True

    b. False

14. Which descriptive nickname was attached to Calgary center Joe Nieuwendyk?

    a. "Broadway Joe"

    b. "Joe Schmoe"

    c. "Classy Joe"

    d. "Crazy Joe"

15. Why did teammates call Flames forward Doug Gilmour by the nickname "Killer"?

    a. They thought he resembled famous serial killer Charles Manson.

    b. He disposed of rats in the arena by using his slapshot.

    c. The name is short for "Ladykiller," because Gilmour was notoriously smooth with women.

    d. He has a tattoo of the word inked on his right bicep.

16. What action, named after Flames defenseman Dion Phaneuf, was quickly dubbed a "Double Dion"?

    a. Scoring two goals and participating in two fights within the same game.
    b. Remaining both expressionless and silent during a post-game press conference.
    c. Punching an opponent with both hands at the same time.
    d. Throwing a body check that knocks down two players at once.

17. Goaltender Mike Smith was kidded by teammates for his common name; so much so that they began called him "Generic."

    a. True
    b. False

18. Atlanta and Calgary Flames winger Eric Vail burst into the NHL, winning the Calder Trophy and going by which entertaining nickname?

    a. "Big Train"
    b. "Sasquatch"
    c. "The Role Model"
    d. "Nightmare"

19. Why was star Calgary defenseman Al MacInnis nicknamed "Chopper"?

    a. He tended to hack and slash opposing forwards in front of his team's net.

b. He began his career with a slow, choppy skating style.

c. He collected Harley Davidson motorcycles, which he raced as a hobby.

d. He showed up to training camp one year in a privately rented helicopter.

20. Flames forward James Neal was known by multiple nicknames throughout his career. Which of the following was NOT one of them?

    a. "Lazy"
    b. "Big Game James"
    c. "Jimmy Glove Side"
    d. "The Real Deal"

21. When Brent Sutter became head coach of the Flames, players joking referred to him as "number 3," because his brothers Brian and Darryl had coached the team previously.

    a. True
    b. False

QUIZ ANSWERS

1. D – "Flaming Snot Donkeys"

2. B – False

3. D – Bill Murray in *Kingpin*

4. C – Mikael Backlund, Michael Frolík, and Matthew Tkachuk

5. B – Guy Chouinard

6. A – "Pepper"

7. B – False

8. B – He had fantastic puck skills and could make the puck do things that other players couldn't.

9. B – "The Grim Reaper"

10. D – He preferred cooking his own pasta on the minor-league team bus rather than eating at restaurants.

11. B – Jarome Iginla

12. A – True

13. C – "Classy Joe"

14. A – They thought he resembled famous serial killer Charles Manson.

15. D – Throwing a body check that knocks down two players at once.

16. B – False

17. A – "Big Train"

18. B – He began his career with a slow, choppy skating style.

19. C – "Jimmy Glove Side"

20. B – False

DID YOU KNOW?

1. Winger Joe Mullen was called "Slippery Rock Joe" for his agility in avoiding hits and balance when absorbing them (which he partially developed through playing roller hockey as a child).

2. Calgary bench boss Mike Keenan was given the nickname "Captain Hook." This did not refer to a clutch-and-grab defensive style of coaching, as many thought, but rather because he was quick to pull a goaltender he did not feel was performing well.

3. Steady but unspectacular center Bill Clement played a reliable game on the ice for Calgary. His detractors poked fun at his lack of high-end ability by chanting "Clement, Clement, hands of cement," which was later mocked in a popular beer commercial.

4. Short-term Flames goalie Curtis Joseph went by the nickname "Cujo," which was an obvious combination of syllables from his first and last name, but also an allusion to the terrifying St. Bernard in horror author Stephen King's tale of a rabid dog who traps a family. Joseph's mask used the frightening dog's image to great effect.

5. Since Brett Hull was traded away from Calgary early in his career, fans never got to see much of "The Golden Brett." Hull took his nickname from his blond hair and as a play on his father Bobby Hull's nickname, "The Golden Jet."

6. Flames left winger Steve Bozek was given the nickname "Boom Boom" due to his hard-nosed style of play and high energy level.

7. Calgary coach Bill Peters liked forward Elias Lindholm's game so much that he often referred to Lindholm in interviews as "The Swedish Beast" or "The Beast," for short.

8. During the Flames' run to the Stanley Cup Finals in 2004, winger Martin Gelinas scored the series-clinching goals against Vancouver, Detroit, and San Jose. His clutch marksmanship earned him the nickname "The Eliminator."

9. Calgary left winger Johnny Gaudreau has gone so far as to trademark his nickname, "Johnny Hockey," stating that he wanted to protect his reputation and control any marketing associated with the name.

10. Current Flames netminder David Rittich has plenty of confidence, a relaxed attitude, and a tendency to thrive in critical situations, qualities that have led to his nickname of "Big Save Dave."

CHAPTER 4:

THE CAPTAIN CLASS

QUIZ TIME!

1. Which player was honored by being named the first captain of the Calgary Flames in 1980-81?

    a. Brad Marsh

    b. Jean Pronovost

    c. Lanny McDonald

    d. Tom Lysiak

2. The Flames have never named a Russian player even as an assistant captain, let alone a captain.

    a. True

    b. False

3. Which captain holds the record for most points in a season while leading the Flames, with 98?

    a. Joe Nieuwendyk

    b. Lanny McDonald

    c. Jarome Iginla

    d. Theoren Fleury

4. Aside from Canada, which country have the Flames most frequently chosen their assistant captains from?

   a. Finland
   b. United States of America
   c. Sweden
   d. Czech Republic

5. How did Flames star Jarome Iginla earn a promotion to captain from previous Calgary captain Craig Conroy?

   a. Conroy was traded to the St. Louis Blues.
   b. Conroy left as a free agent to sign with the Los Angeles Kings.
   c. Conroy was injured and missed a month with a pulled muscle.
   d. Conroy volunteered to step down because Iginla was ready to lead.

6. Which player was the oldest to wear the "C" for the Calgary Flames, at 37 years old?

   a. Mark Giordano
   b. Dave Lowry
   c. Steve Smith
   d. Lanny McDonald

7. In their entire history, the Calgary Flames have never named a goaltender captain of the team.

   a. True
   b. False

8. About which Flames captain, noted for his work ethic, did his coach say, "If you're not practicing what you preach, then I'm not sure your guys are going to buy in. But _____ works a lot harder than he preaches."?

    a. Jarome Iginla

    b. Theoren Fleury

    c. Mark Giordano

    d. Al MacInnis

9. Which Flame set the franchise record for most penalty minutes in a season by a Calgary captain?

    a. Tim Hunter

    b. Jim Peplinski

    c. Bob Boughner

    d. Theoren Fleury

10. Dave Lowry recorded the lowest plus/minus season for any Calgary captain in 2001-02. How low did he finish?

    a. -11

    b. -14

    c. -18

    d. -20

11. How many consecutive times did prolific Flames captain Jarome Iginla score 30 or more goals in a single season?

    a. 3

    b. 6

    c. 9

    d. 11

12. For three seasons in the 1990s, Calgary elected not to name a captain. Instead, they had a rotation of players who wore an "A" (usually designated for assistant captains) with three sporting the letter in each game.

    a. True

    b. False

13. Which of the following players was NOT one of the Flames' "tri-captains" for the Calgary team that lost the 1986 Stanley Cup Final to Montreal?

    a. Doug Risebrough

    b. Joel Otto

    c. Lanny McDonald

    d. Jim Peplinski

14. How many players that have held the Flames' captaincy have been elected to the Hockey Hall of Fame?

    a. 0

    b. 1

    c. 2

    d. 3

15. In which year did the Flames name their first captain who was NOT born in Canada?

    a. 1981 – Phil Russell

    b. 1999 – Steve Smith

    c. 2001 – Craig Conroy

    d. The Flames have always had a Canadian captain.

16. During their entire history, the Calgary Flames have elected only one defenseman to be the captain of the team.

    a. True
    b. False

17. One Flames captain has played for seven NHL teams, more than any other franchise leader. Who was this well-traveled player?

    a. Brad Marsh
    b. Bob Boughner
    c. Todd Simpson
    d. Steve Smith

18. Which Flame was the youngest player in the team's history to be made captain, taking the leadership mantle at just 22 years old?

    a. Jim Peplinski
    b. Todd Simpson
    c. Brad Marsh
    d. Jarome Iginla

19. The team has had some great leaders who were never given the formal responsibility of being the Flames' captain. Which player is the only one on the list to wear the "C"?

    a. Tim Hunter
    b. Joel Otto
    c. Gary Roberts
    d. Matthew Tkachuk

20. In Joe Nieuwendyk and Jarome Iginla, who were traded for each other, the Flames boast the two longest-serving captains (measured by seasons played while captain of the team) in NHL history.

    a. True

    b. False

QUIZ ANSWERS

1. A – Brad Marsh

2. B – False

3. C – Jarome Iginla

4. B – United States of America

5. D – Conroy volunteered to step down because Iginla was ready to lead.

6. C – Steve Smith

7. A – True

8. C – Mark Giordano

9. A – Tim Hunter

10. D – -20

11. D – 11

12. B – False

13. B – Joel Otto

14. D – 3

15. B – 1999 – Steve Smith

16. B – False

17. C – Todd Simpson

18. C – Brad Marsh

19. A – Tim Hunter

20. B – False

DID YOU KNOW?

1. The Flames named Jarome Iginla captain in 2003, making him just the second black captain in NHL history. Chicago Blackhawks forward Dirk Graham was the first when he was given the "C" in the 1988-89 season.

2. Flames captain Jim Peplinski was not afraid to demonstrate his leadership with rugged play when necessary. Among Calgary captains, Peplinski recorded four of the top five seasons with the highest penalty minutes recorded; each of those seasons was between 1985-86 and 1988-89.

3. Some players did not want the captaincy of the Flames. Winger Theo Fleury was the fairly obvious choice after the previous captain, Joe Nieuwendyk, was traded to Dallas in 1995. But Fleury felt that the captaincy was bad for his game and personal relationships with his coach and teammates, so he gave up the "C" after two seasons.

4. Two Calgary Flames captains represented Team Canada in the 1998 Winter Olympic Games in Nagano, Japan; the first time NHL players were allowed to participate. Both center Joe Nieuwendyk and right winger Theoren Fleury represented Canada. Canada's "dream team" was eliminated on a shootout goal by Calgary forward Robert Reichel as his Czech Republic team went on to a gold medal victory.

5. Robert Reichel's memorable Olympic moments continued in 2002, when his Czech Republic team faced off against

Germany. This was notable because Reichel's brother Martin was on the German team, marking only the second time in Olympic hockey that two brothers had squared off against each other.

6. Flames captain Jim Peplinski played his entire NHL career with Calgary. Not only was he loyal, but he was also reliable, as he played 711 games for the franchise while missing only 24.

7. Calgary captain Jarome Iginla was well-liked as a kind and generous person. He has donated over a million dollars to charity and sees spur-of-the-moment opportunities to chip in as well. During the 2002 Olympics, he chatted with four fans from Calgary at a restaurant who were sleeping in their car. Iginla quietly rented a hotel room for them at his own expense.

8. When the franchise moved from Atlanta to Calgary, it was a culture shock for many players. Instead of warm weather and relaxed attitudes, they faced Canadian winters and a passionate fan base, which a lot of the team struggled with. GM Cliff Fletcher decided to trade for Lanny McDonald to bring in his leadership and character. The move worked, as the Flames performed well and their captain, McDonald, eventually led them to a Stanley Cup.

9. Two of the most respected players in the NHL shared a nice moment in 2008. Long-time Vancouver Canucks captain Trevor Linden retired following a game with the Flames, and Calgary captain Jarome Iginla led the whole

squad in a line to shake Linden's hand and wish him well. Linden remarked, "I think Jarome is one of the most classy players in the league."

10. Jarome Iginla has served the longest tenure as Flames captain. He wore the "C" for nine seasons between 2003 and 2013 before being traded elsewhere. Current captain Mark Giordano has held the position for seven seasons and has a chance to pass Iginla.

CHAPTER 5:

STATISTICALLY SPEAKING

QUIZ TIME!

1. What is Calgary's franchise record for most victories in a single regular season?

    a. 48

    b. 50

    c. 52

    d. 54

2. No one in Flames history is within 100 assists of Al MacInnis at the top of Calgary's record book.

    a. True

    b. False

3. Four goalies have recorded over 100 career wins for the Flames. Which one of them has the most?

    a. Miikka Kiprusoff

    b. Dan Bouchard

    c. Reggie Lemelin

    d. Mike Vernon

4. Who is the Flames' single-season leader in goals scored, with 66?

   a. Jarome Iginla
   b. Theoren Fleury
   c. Joe Mullen
   d. Lanny McDonald

5. Which Flame really made his shots count, showing his accuracy with the highest career shooting percentage for the team by almost 3% over his nearest competitor?

   a. Craig Conroy
   b. Curtis Glencross
   c. Sergei Makarov
   d. Kent Nilsson

6. The most penalty minutes recorded in any season by a Flames player is 375. Who established this club record?

   a. Ron Stern
   b. Tim Hunter
   c. Gary Roberts
   d. Neil Sheehy

7. The highest ever Flames plus/minus in a single game was +9, recorded by right winger Theoren Fleury in a 13-1 victory over the San Jose Sharks.

   a. True
   b. False

8. Which goaltender holds the Calgary record for most wins in a single season, with 45?

a. Mike Vernon

b. Mike Smith

c. Miikka Kiprusoff

d. Fred Brathwaite

9. Which Flame has played more NHL games with the franchise than any other player?

a. Jarome Iginla

b. Theoren Fleury

c. Mark Giordano

d. Robyn Regehr

10. The talented Jarome Iginla is Calgary's all-time leader in goals scored. How many goals did he score for the team?

a. 425

b. 501

c. 525

d. 603

11. Who holds the single-season Flames record for points per game, at 1.64?

a. Kent Nilsson

b. Joe Nieuwendyk

c. Theoren Fleury

d. Joe Mullen

12. By the advanced stat metric "goals created per game," Håkan Loob was responsible for generating more goals per game than any other Flame.

a. True

b. False

13. Which Flames defenseman has recorded the most points while playing with the club?

    a. Phil Housley
    b. Gary Suter
    c. Mark Giordano
    d. Al MacInnis

14. How many Flames have reached the 100-point mark in a single NHL season?

    a. 4
    b. 6
    c. 8
    d. 10

15. How many Flames have fired over 2,000 shots on net for the club during their careers?

    a. 1
    b. 2
    c. 3
    d. 7

16. Winger Joe Mullen posted a +51 rating during the 1988-89 season, which remains a franchise record.

    a. True
    b. False

17. Which Flame recorded the highest career plus/minus with Calgary, with a +239 rating?

    a. Brad McCrimmon
    b. Gary Roberts

c. Jamie Macoun

d. Al MacInnis

18. Which Flame recorded the most game-winning goals for the team, scoring 83?

   a. Theoren Fleury

   b. Jarome Iginla

   c. Joe Nieuwendyk

   d. Lanny McDonald

19. Which two teammates posted the highest combined point total in a season for the Flames franchise?

   a. Håkan Loob and Mike Bullard in 1987-88

   b. Al MacInnis and Theoren Fleury in 1990-91

   c. Bob MacMillan and Guy Chouinard in 1978-79

   d. Jarome Iginla and Daymond Langkow in 2005-06

20. Goalie Miikka Kiprusoff's 2006-07 season is the benchmark in terms of shots faced, as he faced 2,190, and six of his other seasons follow behind before any other netminder comes close.

   a. True

   b. False

QUIZ ANSWERS

1. D – 54

2. B – False

3. A – Miikka Kiprusoff

4. D – Lanny McDonald

5. C – Sergei Makarov

6. B – Tim Hunter

7. A – True

8. C – Miikka Kiprusoff

9. A – Jarome Iginla

10. C – 525

11. A – Kent Nilsson

12. B – False

13. D – Al MacInnis

14. C – 8

15. C – 3

16. A – True

17. D – Al MacInnis

18. B – Jarome Iginla

19. C – Bob MacMillan and Guy Chouinard in 1978-79

20. A – True

DID YOU KNOW?

1. Just one player has scored more than 1,000 points with the Flames franchise. Stalwart winger Jarome Iginla broke Theoren Fleury's previous record of 830 and finished with 1,095 total.

2. NHL icon Jaromir Jagr ranks second on the all-time list for most career points in the league, with 1,921. Sadly for the Flames, only seven of those came while he was with their team.

3. Not counting seasons shortened by a lockout, the 2003-04 Flames were the stingiest version of the club to ever take the ice. They allowed only 176 goals against during the entire year; that's the only time the club has been under 200.

4. Theoren Fleury was a force on the penalty kill for the Flames, using his speed to cover ground quickly. In a 1991 game against the St. Louis Blues, Fleury set an NHL record by scoring a hat trick of all short-handed goals.

5. Kent Nilsson often scored in bunches, recording 14 hat tricks (scoring three goals in the same game), during his Calgary career. The next closest Flame is Theoren Fleury, who finished just behind, with 13.

6. Winger Tim Hunter dominates the Calgary record books when it comes to penalty minutes. He holds the top team marks for PIM during a regular season, a playoff season,

51

and a career. Hunter twice led the league in penalty minutes for a season and once recorded the most in a playoff season. His 3,142 career penalty minutes (2,405 with the Flames) rank him eighth overall in NHL history.

7. The team record for most points in a season is 131, set by center Kent Nilsson. Remarkably, he set this record in the team's very first season in Calgary, and it has never been broken. During the same year, he also established the still-standing team record for most assists in a season, with 82, and the most points ever scored in a season by a Swedish NHL player.

8. The most recent time the Flames scored more than 300 goals in a season was 1993-94, when they tallied 302. This was still a big drop from the team record of 397, set in 1987-88.

9. One of the deadliest Flames on the power play was Joe Nieuwendyk. He led the NHL in 1987-88 with 31 power-play goals (which remains a team record) and finished in the top 10 in the league on multiple other occasions.

10. In 1995-96, Theoren Fleury fired 353 shots on net, establishing the Flames record for most shots taken by one player in a single season. He scored 46 times, which was a fairly low 13% shooting percentage.

CHAPTER 6:

THE TRADE MARKET

QUIZ TIME!

1. Which player acquired from the Toronto Maple Leafs in the Dion Phaneuf trade of 2010 lasted longest with the Flames?

    a. Niklas Hagman
    b. Ian White
    c. Jamal Mayers
    d. Matt Stajan

2. In 2018-19, Cam Talbot was in net for the Edmonton Oilers, and Mike Smith manned the crease for the Calgary Flames. In 2019-20, Talbot was on Calgary and Smith was on Edmonton, but the two were not traded for each other.

    a. True
    b. False

3. In 2017, the Flames traded three draft choices to the New York Islanders to secure a player from Manitoba who wanted to be closer to home for family reasons. Which player was this?

a. Defenseman Travis Hamonic

b. Center Mark Jankowski

c. Defenseman Rhett Warrener

d. Goalie Mike Smith

4. The Calgary Flames twice traded center Jason Wiemer, once with teammate Valeri Bure for Rob Niedermayer and once for a 4th round draft pick. Which teams did they deal Wiemer to?

a. Tampa Bay Lightning and Minnesota Wild

b. New York Islanders and New Jersey Devils

c. Florida Panthers and New Jersey Devils

d. Tampa Bay Lightning and Columbus Blue Jackets

5. Which useful Flames player was NOT received from the Hartford Whalers in 1994 in exchange for Gary Suter, Paul Ranheim, and Ted Drury?

a. Michael Nylander

b. Steve Chiasson

c. Zarley Zalapski

d. James Patrick

6. One of the Flames' best trades saw them acquire Doug Gilmour, Mark Hunter, Steve Bozek, and Michael Dark, in exchange for Mike Bullard, Tim Corkery, and Craig Coxe. Which team regretted making that deal with Calgary?

a. Toronto Maple Leafs

b. New Jersey Devils

c. Chicago Blackhawks

d. St. Louis Blues

7. Calgary has completed more trades with the Montreal Canadiens than with any other NHL franchise.

   a. True
   b. False

8. In what year did the Flames first make a trade for "future considerations," who did they trade with, and what did those considerations turn out to be?

   a. 1992, Chicago Blackhawks, forward Stephane Matteau
   b. 1980, Washington Capitals, cash
   c. 1986, Quebec Nordiques, a 7th round draft choice
   d. 1998, New York Rangers, cash

9. During their history, the Flames have given up too early on a few players who turned out to be stars in the NHL. Which of the following players did they NOT trade away before the player blossomed?

   a. Center Marc Savard
   b. Winger Brett Hull
   c. Winger Martin St. Louis
   d. Center Tyler Seguin

10. Who did the Calgary Flames select with the first draft pick acquired by the team, a 1982 2nd round pick from the Boston Bruins that landed at 39th overall?

   a. Center Bill Clement
   b. Goalie Rick Wamsley
   c. Defenseman Steve Konroyd
   d. Winger Jacques Richard

11. In 2013, the Flames traded long-time captain Jarome Iginla to give him a better shot at chasing a Stanley Cup ring. Their underwhelming trade return from Boston featured three players; how many combined NHL games did those players suit up for with Calgary?

    a. 0
    b. 27
    c. 62
    d. 103

12. Calgary has never in its history completed a trade with the Vegas Golden Knights.

    a. True
    b. False

13. Who did the Flames give up in the deal that saw them acquire franchise icon Lanny McDonald from the Colorado Rockies?

    a. Center Mel Bridgman
    b. Right winger Willi Plett, a 1st round draft pick, and cash
    c. Wingers Don Lever and Bob MacMillan
    d. Goaltender Don Edwards and two 2nd round draft picks

14. Who or what did the Flames give up to the San Jose Sharks in return for the top goalie in franchise history, Miikka Kiprusoff?

    a. Defenseman Derek Morris and goaltender Roman Turek

b. A 1st round draft choice and winger Kristian Huselius

c. Center Jeff Shantz and defenseman Rhett Warrener

d. A 2nd round draft choice

15. In gearing up for a 2020 playoff run, the Flames gave up draft choices to Los Angeles and Chicago for which two players who would form a defensive pairing for the Flames?

a. Rasmus Andersson and Juuso Valimaki

b. Derek Forbort and Erik Gustafsson

c. Noah Hanifin and Travis Hamonic

d. T.J. Brodie and Mark Giordano

16. After leaving Calgary to sign with the Los Angeles Kings as a free agent, the Kings traded center Craig Conroy back to Calgary where he happily scored two goals in his first game back with the Flames…in a win over the Kings.

a. True

b. False

17. One of the Flames' busiest periods was the three days from June 7 to 9, 1982. How many players and draft picks were involved in trades made by Calgary during that time?

a. 6 players and 4 draft picks

b. 7 players and 8 draft picks

c. 8 players and 3 draft picks

d. 9 players and 10 draft picks

18. In 2015, Calgary gave up a 1st round pick and two 2nd round picks for which young player?

    a. Boston defender Dougie Hamilton
    b. St. Louis defender Jay Bouwmeester
    c. Colorado forward Alex Tanguay
    d. Montreal forward Mike Cammalleri

19. In 2018, Calgary acquired young and cost-controlled Elias Lindholm and Noah Hanifin from the Carolina Hurricanes. Which of the following players did they NOT have to give up in the deal?

    a. Forward Micheal Ferland
    b. Defenseman Adam Fox
    c. Forward James Neal
    d. Defenseman Dougie Hamilton

20. The Flames' deal to acquire center Olli Jokinen from the Phoenix Coyotes paid immediate dividends, as Jokinen tallied 10 points during his first half dozen games with the club, and was the NHL's Second Star of the Week.

    a. True
    b. False

QUIZ ANSWERS

1. D – Matt Stajan

2. A – True

3. A – Defenseman Travis Hamonic

4. C – Florida Panthers and New Jersey Devils

5. B – Steve Chiasson

6. D – St. Louis Blues

7. B – False

8. B – 1980, Washington Capitals, cash

9. D – Center Tyler Seguin

10. C – Defenseman Steve Konroyd

11. B – 27

12. A – True

13. C – Wingers Don Lever and Bob MacMillan

14. D – A 2nd round draft choice

15. B – Derek Forbort and Erik Gustafsson

16. A – True

17. D – 9 players and 10 draft picks

18. A – Boston defender Dougie Hamilton

19. C – Forward James Neal

20. A – True

DID YOU KNOW?

1. After it was announced that the Atlanta Flames would be moving to Calgary, the team got ready for the move by making a few trades. Their first as the Calgary Flames was very significant, as they sent Olympic hero goalie Jim Craig to the Boston Bruins for two draft choices that would become Steve Konroyd and hometown hero goalie Mike Vernon.

2. During their history, the Flames have traded for some famous Hall of Fame names… Unfortunately, they did not get the players who made the names famous. Calgary has dealt for not quite superstars Valeri (not Pavel) Bure, Rob (not Scott) Niedermayer, Nicolas (not Gilbert) Perreault, and Jocelyn (not Mario) Lemieux.

3. One interesting Calgary trade tree leads through three generations of Calgary superstars. Arguably the team's first star, Kent Nilsson, was traded to the Minnesota North Stars for a draft pick that was used on Joe Nieuwendyk. After Nieuwendyk excelled for years for the Flames, he was dealt to the same franchise (now relocated as the Dallas Stars) for a young player who would go on to become another franchise icon, Jarome Iginla.

4. Winger Alex Tanguay liked the Calgary Flames' organization but requested a trade because his offensive playing style didn't mesh well with Coach Mike Keenan's

defensive use of him. Calgary obliged and dealt him to Montreal for a 1st and 2nd round draft choice. Tanguay later re-signed with the Flames as a free agent and thrived under new coach Brent Sutter's system.

5. At the 2010 NHL trade deadline, center Olli Jokinen leaned that the Flames were dealing him to the New York Rangers. However, the team would not finalize the deal immediately because they did not have a replacement player available for their game that day. So, Jokinen played his final game in Calgary knowing that it was his last and he would be headed to New York immediately afterward.

6. Although fan reaction was unfavorable at first when the Flames traded leading scorer Cory Stillman to St. Louis for Craig Conroy, Conroy would become an excellent sidekick to Jarome Iginla, as well as providing leadership in the locker room and well-rounded play on the ice. He became a beloved figure in Calgary and remains so to this day after settling there with his family.

7. One of the worst trades made by the Flames occurred in 1992 when they sent Doug Gilmour, Rick Wamsley, Ric Nattress, Kent Manderville, and Jamie Macoun to the Toronto Maple Leafs after arguments over Gilmour's salary demands. Toronto soared in the standings, but Calgary received no impact players in the deal, getting just Michel Petit, Jeff Reese, Gary Leeman, Craig Berube, and Alexander Godynyuk. None of these players lasted more than two years with the Flames.

8. The Gilmour trade mentioned above set the record as the largest trade in NHL history. In all, 10 players were involved in the deal.

9. For 30 years, the Flames and their provincial rival, the Edmonton Oilers, refused to complete a trade. The first-ever transaction between the clubs took place in 2010 and saw the Oilers send defenseman Steve Staios to Calgary for defenseman Aaron Johnson and a 3rd round draft choice.

10. Being dealt was a double-edged sword for Flames goalie Reggie Lemelin. The Flames traded him to the Bruins in 1987-88 after Mike Vernon won the starting job in Calgary. Lemelin thus missed out on winning a Stanley Cup in 1989 but did enjoy his own success, teaming with Andy Moog in Boston to take home the William M. Jennings Trophy for fewest goals allowed.

CHAPTER 7:

DRAFT DAY

QUIZ TIME!

1. When the city of Calgary hosted the NHL Entry Draft in 2000, which prospect did the Flames draft with their 1st round pick in front of the hometown fans?

    a. Left winger Eric Nystrom
    b. Goalie Brent Krahn
    c. Right winger Chuck Kobasew
    d. Nobody – they had traded the pick for center Marc Savard.

2. The Flames have never picked higher than 4th overall in the NHL Draft in the entire history of the franchise.

    a. True
    b. False

3. How high did Calgary select defenseman Gary Suter in the 1984 NHL Entry Draft, before Suter went on to win the Calder Trophy as rookie of the year?

    a. 1st round, 5th overall
    b. 2nd round, 43rd overall

c. 9th round, 180th overall

d. 12th round, 22nd overall

4. Which center did the Flames select highest in the NHL Entry Draft, using a 4th overall pick to add the player to their team?

   a. Daniel Tkaczuk

   b. Dan Quinn

   c. Sam Bennett

   d. Sean Monahan

5. Who was the first player ever selected by the Calgary Flames in the NHL Entry Draft?

   a. Defenseman Paul Reinhart

   b. Defenseman Steve Konroyd

   c. Left winger Richard Kromm

   d. Right winger Denis Cyr

6. Which player, drafted by the Flames, went on to score the most NHL points for another team?

   a. Joe Nieuwendyk

   b. Brett Hull

   c. Al MacInnis

   d. Brian Bradley

7. Calgary has drafted precisely 11 players who have played just one game in the NHL. None of the skaters have scored a point, and none of the goalies have recorded a win.

   a. True

   b. False

8. In which year did the Flames select eight players who skated for at least one game in the NHL, the most in franchise history?

   a. 1981
   b. 1986
   c. 1992
   d. 2007

9. Fan favorite Theoren Fleury was selected in the 8th round by the Calgary Flames in 1987. Which junior league did he play in?

   a. Ontario Hockey League
   b. East Coast Hockey League
   c. Quebec Major Junior Hockey League
   d. Western Hockey League

10. Who was the first player ever drafted by the Calgary Flames who did NOT play for a Canadian junior team?

    a. Right winger Håkan Loob
    b. Defenseman Randy Turnbull
    c. Defenseman Rick Heppner
    d. Right winger Sergei Makarov

11. The Vegas Golden Knights selected which Calgary Flame in the 2017 Expansion Draft, who happened to live in Las Vegas during the off-season?

    a. Left winger James Neal
    b. Center Cody Eakin
    c. Left winger William Carrier
    d. Defenseman Deryk Engelland

12. General manager Cliff Fletcher drafted Russian star Sergei Makarov in 1983, but it was not until 1989 that Makarov was allowed to come to Canada to join the Flames.

    a. True
    b. False

13. The Flames struck out mightily in the 2006 NHL Draft, selecting seven skaters who scored a total of how many NHL goals?

    a. 0
    b. 19
    c. 36
    d. 50

14. When the Flames selected center Brett Sutter 179th overall in the 2005 NHL Entry Draft, they were selecting the son of which famous Sutter brother who worked for the team and had been selected at the exact same 179th spot in the 1978 NHL Entry Draft?

    a. Darryl Sutter
    b. Brent Sutter
    c. Duane Sutter
    d. Ron Sutter

15. Star defenseman Dion Phaneuf was drafted by Calgary 9th overall in the 2003 NHL Entry Draft. Which other defenders were selected ahead of him?

    a. Brent Seabrook and Mark Stuart
    b. Ryan Suter and Braydon Coburn

   c. Cam Barker and Ladislav Smid

   d. Joni Pitkänen and Ryan Whitney

16. The Flames selected yet another Sutter, right winger Shaun Sutter, in the 1998 NHL Entry Draft, but he never skated with the team.

   a. True

   b. False

17. Up to and including the 2019 NHL Entry Draft, how many player selections have the Calgary Flames made in their history?

   a. 370

   b. 412

   c. 456

   d. 592

18. Which position has Calgary traditionally put a premium on, by drafting it most frequently when they've held a top 10 overall draft pick?

   a. Center

   b. Left wing

   c. Right wing

   d. Defense

19. What is the lowest position in the draft that the Flames have selected a player who would go on to make the Hockey Hall of Fame?

   a. 26th overall

   b. 94th overall

c. 160th overall

d. 231st overall

20. Center Matthew Lombardi was instantly endeared to Flames fans because he was initially drafted by the Edmonton Oilers, refused to sign with them, and re-entered the draft where he was picked by Calgary instead.

a. True

b. False

QUIZ ANSWERS

1. B – Goalie Brent Krahn

2. A – True

3. C – 9th round, 180th overall

4. C – Sam Bennett

5. D – Right winger Dennis Cyr

6. B – Brett Hull

7. A – True

8. C – 1992

9. D – Western Hockey League

10. B – Defenseman Randy Turnbull

11. D – Defenseman Deryk Engelland

12. A – True

13. A – 0

14. A – Darryl Sutter

15. B – Ryan Suter and Braydon Coburn

16. A – True

17. C – 456

18. A – Center

19. D – 231st overall

20. A – True

DID YOU KNOW?

1. Between 1999 and 2003, Calgary enjoyed a stretch in which they selected at least one player each year who lasted 500 games in the NHL. During those years, they hit on: Craig Anderson, Travis Moen, Jarret Stoll, Dave Moss, Chuck Kobasew, Matthew Lombardi, Eric Nystrom, and Dion Phaneuf.

2. When the Iron Curtain fell, the Flames jumped into the newfound player pool quickly, selecting eight Russians, one German, one Slovak, and nine Czechs by the end of 1992.

3. Flames mainstay and long-time captain Mark Giordano actually went undrafted by any team in the NHL. He signed as a free agent with the Flames in 2004 and was a bit of a late bloomer, winning the Norris Trophy in 2019 when he was 35 years old.

4. Great scouting helped Calgary turn in one of the NHL's best draft classes of all time in 1984. That class yielded four skaters who played over 1,000 NHL games: Gary Roberts in the 1st round, Paul Ranheim in the 2nd, Brett Hull in the 6th, and Gary Suter in the 9th.

5. The first Flames draft pick who went on to play 1,000 NHL games was defenseman Al MacInnis, who the team took 15th overall in 1981. MacInnis lasted 1,416 games in the league and won the Conn Smythe Trophy with Calgary in 1989.

6. The Flames did not put much stock in the 2014 NHL Scouting Combine. Center prospect Sam Bennett could not manage to do a single pull-up at the event, but Calgary chose him 4th overall, nonetheless. Bennett went on to become a key playoff contributor for the Flames.

7. The largest Flames draft classes ever yielded 14 players apiece. Calgary had these record hauls in 1982, 1983, and 1991. They fared best in 1983 when four of the 14 went on to lengthy, distinguished careers (Dan Quinn, Brian Bradley, Perry Berezan, and Sergei Makarov), but largely struck out in 1991 when only Sandy McCarthy made a major impact.

8. Calgary has drafted two players who went on to record over 2,000 penalty minutes in the NHL. Despite being taken in back-to-back years (1984 & 1985) and both playing left wing, the two players could hardly be more different. Gary Roberts was chosen 12th overall and was a premier power forward, scoring 909 points to go along with his 2,560 penalty minutes. Stu Grimson was taken 143rd overall and was mainly an enforcer, recording 2,113 PIM, but only 39 points.

9. The Flames drafted goalie Trevor Kidd 11th overall in the 1990 NHL Draft, but they would probably like a do-over on that pick. Kidd was the first goaltender off the board, so Calgary had its choice of any netminder and selected Kidd over the other top option: Martin Brodeur. Brodeur was selected 20th overall by the New Jersey Devils and went on to become the winningest goalie in NHL history.

10. The latest draft choice the Flames have made was 279th overall. They've held this late pick twice, a decade apart. In 1994, they used it on Russian center Pavel Torgayev, and in 2004, they chose Canadian right winger Adam Cracknell. Against the odds, both players would see time in the NHL, with Cracknell having the better career of the two.

CHAPTER 8:

GOALTENDER TIDBITS

QUIZ TIME!

1. Who was the regular starting goalie for Calgary during the team's challenging first season in Alberta, in 1980-81?

    a. Rick Tabaracci

    b. Dan Bouchard

    c. Reggie Lemelin

    d. Pat Riggin

2. No Calgary netminder has ever faced a penalty shot in overtime of a Stanley Cup playoff game.

    a. True

    b. False

3. Which goaltender has recorded the most career wins and shutouts while with the Calgary Flames?

    a. Mike Vernon

    b. Dan Bouchard

    c. Miikka Kiprusoff

    d. Trevor Kidd

4. After two playing stints with Calgary, goalie Jamie McLennan worked for the team in all of the following positions except for which one?

    a. Professional scout
    b. Assistant general manager
    c. Director of goaltender development
    d. Assistant coach

5. In 2003-04, Flames goalie Miikka Kiprusoff set the modern era NHL record for lowest goals-against average. Just how low was his GAA?

    a. 2.11
    b. 1.95
    c. 1.82
    d. 1.69

6. Flames goaltender Brian Elliott learned which unusual skill from a former champion in the sport?

    a. Moose calling
    b. Pogo stick jumping
    c. Competitive bartending
    d. Skeet shooting

7. It is a Flames tradition for every goaltender to tap both posts and the crossbar with his stick following the warm-up before a game.

    a. True
    b. False

8. Which of the following is NOT true about quirky Flames goaltender Miikka Kiprusoff?

    a. He recorded the first-ever outdoor shutout in the NHL, in the 2011 Heritage Classic.

    b. He once rejected a trade to the Toronto Maple Leafs, preferring to stay in Calgary.

    c. He played one period of the 2012 NHL All-Star Game with an old-school facemask rather than a full helmet.

    d. He stopped two penalty shots in one game against Columbus; the first time a goalie had done so in a quarter-century.

9. Who was the backup goaltender for the Flames when they won the Stanley Cup in 1989?

    a. Ken Wregget

    b. Reggie Lemelin

    c. Rick Wamsley

    d. Phil Myre

10. Flames goalie Mike Vernon recorded his first NHL win and first NHL shutout against the same NHL team in two separate games. Which team did he face?

    a. Winnipeg Jets

    b. Edmonton Oilers

    c. Vancouver Canucks

    d. Montreal Canadiens

11. Why did Miikka Kiprusoff replace Jamie McLennan between the Calgary pipes just 18 seconds after Kiprusoff had been yanked for giving up five goals in a game against the Detroit Red Wings?

a. Kiprusoff convincingly argued to coach Darryl Sutter that he needed the work to stay sharp for the upcoming playoffs.

b. McLennan was scored on twice during those 18 seconds.

c. McLennan was injured when opposing forward Henrik Zetterberg fell on him in the crease.

d. McLennan was ejected for slashing opposing forward Johan Franzen.

12. Reggie Lemelin's playoff save percentage was lower than his regular-season save percentage in every year he played with the Flames.

a. True

b. False

13. During the 1989 Stanley Cup playoffs, goalie Mike Vernon made an incredible breakaway save that came to be known as "the save that won the Cup." Who did he stop?

a. Jimmy Carson of the Los Angeles Kings

b. Steve Larmer of the Chicago Blackhawks

c. Stephane Richer of the Montreal Canadiens

d. Stan Smyl of the Vancouver Canucks

14. Which goaltender earned his 400th career win while playing for Calgary, though he had just five wins with the team overall?

a. Jean-Sebastien Giguère

b. Curtis Joseph

c. Grant Fuhr

d. Ken Wregget

15. Following the retirement of star goalie Miikka Kiprusoff, which netminder initially won the battle to replace him as the Flames' starter?

    a. Jonas Hiller
    b. Joey McDonald
    c. Reto Berra
    d. Karri Ramo

16. Former Flames goalie Reggie Lemelin was the first goaltender in professional hockey to score a goal.

    a. True
    b. False

17. Which Flames goaltender was born in Calgary, and played his junior hockey with the Calgary Canucks and Wranglers?

    a. Mike Vernon
    b. Fred Brathwaite
    c. Mike Smith
    d. Cam Talbot

18. Calgary goaltender Miikka Kiprusoff played in the 2010 Winter Olympics for which bronze medal-winning team?

    a. Canada
    b. Finland
    c. Sweden
    d. Switzerland

19. Which Flames goalie once appeared in a rap video by Jermaine Dupri called "Welcome to Atlanta"?

a. Grant Fuhr

b. Dwayne Roloson

c. Fred Brathwaite

d. Chad Johnson

20. Mike Vernon's parents stopped attending home games at the Saddledome because Calgary fans would boo and taunt them when Vernon allowed a soft goal.

a. True

b. False

QUIZ ANSWERS

1. D – Pat Riggin

2. B – False

3. C – Miikka Kiprusoff

4. B – Assistant general manager

5. D – 1.69

6. A – Moose calling

7. B – False

8. C – He played one period of the 2012 NHL All-Star Game with an old-school facemask rather than a full helmet.

9. C – Rick Wamsley

10. C – Vancouver Canucks

11. D – McLennan was ejected for slashing opposing forward Johan Franzen.

12. A – True

13. D – Stan Smyl of the Vancouver Canucks

14. C – Grant Fuhr

15. D – Karri Ramo

16. B – False

17. A – Mike Vernon

18. B – Finland

19. C – Fred Brathwaite

20. A – True

DID YOU KNOW?

21. Rick Tabaracci had a long and well-traveled goaltending career. In addition to his four seasons with the Flames, he played for an incredible 17 teams, including 6 others in the NHL, and for squads known as the Waxers, Komets, Pirates, Wolves, Grizzlies, Solar Bears—and two different teams both nicknamed the Lumberjacks.

22. Calgary goaltender Roman Turek had a recurring theme with the artwork on his masks. Turek was a big fan of the British rock group Iron Maiden, so all of his masks incorporated their gruesome-looking mascot, "Eddie," in the design.

23. There have been 15 goals scored by a goaltender in NHL history. Calgary has never been involved in one, either as the team recording the goal or the team being scored upon.

24. Flames goalie Trevor Kidd faced his share of difficult battles for a starting spot during his career. In addition to Stanley Cup winner Mike Vernon in Calgary, Kidd also had to duel with Olympians Sean Burke, Arturs Irbe, Roberto Luongo, and Ed Belfour.

25. The worst goals-against average of any netminder who has played at least a full season's worth of games for the Flames came from Don Edwards between 1983 and 1985. Edwards posted a 4.07 GAA during his time in Calgary

before being sent to the Toronto Maple Leafs to finish his career there.

26. Cam Talbot set the Flames' record for most saves in a single game during an August 16, 2020, playoff matchup against the Dallas Stars. Dallas fired 62 shots, and Talbot turned aside 57 in a 5-4 overtime loss.

27. Only one goalie who has played for the Flames has been enshrined in the Hall of Fame. Grant Fuhr was inducted in 2003, but Calgary fans did not rejoice, as he played just 23 games for the team at the end of his career, and had actually spent a decade tormenting the Flames while with the powerhouse rival Edmonton Oilers.

28. Netminder Dan Bouchard was the last original Atlanta Flame to play with the franchise after it moved to Calgary.

29. Goalies Mike Vernon and Trevor Kidd were entwined throughout their careers. In Calgary, where Vernon had starred for a decade, it was the drafting of Kidd that led to Vernon's trade to the Detroit Red Wings. When Kidd did not work out in Calgary, he ended up playing for the Florida Panthers, where he suffered a shoulder injury that led to Florida acquiring Vernon to fill in. Vernon then finished his career in Calgary after the Panthers chose to keep the younger Kidd.

30. When Calgary obtained little known goalie Miikka Kiprusoff from the San Jose Sharks, he was impressive immediately. "Kipper" won his first game, allowed one goal or less nearly a dozen times, and won NHL Defensive

Player of the Month for his first full month with the club before leading them to within one win of the Stanley Cup.

CHAPTER 9:

ON THE BLUE LINE

QUIZ TIME!

1. Which Flames defenseman was the first blue-liner to lead the NHL in playoff scoring during a postseason run?

    a. Phil Housley
    b. Al MacInnis
    c. Dion Phaneuf
    d. Mark Giordano

2. Flames stalwart Al MacInnis was named godfather to T.J. Brodie's first son, who was also named Al in honor of Brodie's idol on the blue line.

    a. True
    b. False

3. During the 2016 NHL season, Calgary defenseman Dennis Wideman was suspended for 20 games for doing what?

    a. Deliberately running over St. Louis Blues goaltender Jake Allen behind the net
    b. Using a banned substance to gain a competitive advantage

c. Cross-checking a referee from behind and causing a concussion

d. Fighting with Tampa Bay Lightning forward J.T. Miller in a public restaurant

4. Why does Flames defender Mark Giordano touch his stick to his helmet twice after the national anthems are finished?

   a. As a reminder to himself that, without exceptional skill, he needs to work twice as hard as anyone else during the game.

   b. As a superstition, because he did it once before a game in junior hockey and then scored a hat trick.

   c. As a tribute to his sister, who passed away in a car accident when he was a teenager.

   d. As a signal to his mother and father to show them he remembers all the work they put in to help him develop as a young player.

5. Which versatile skater occasionally played his regular spot as a defenseman and took shifts at the center position during the same game?

   a. Phil Housley

   b. Paul Reinhart

   c. Toni Lydman

   d. Pat Quinn

6. Which defender has played more minutes on the Flames blue line than anyone else?

   a. Mark Giordano

   b. T.J. Brodie

c. Gary Suter

d. Dion Phaneuf

7. Gentlemanly player T.J. Brodie has recorded more points than penalty minutes in all but one of his nine full seasons on the Flames blue line.

a. True

b. False

8. What action caused defenseman Gary Suter to receive a death threat from a fan?

a. A scuffle with police who were attempting to arrest fellow defenseman Chris Chelios

b. A "baseball swing" to the face of a Russian player during an international tournament, resulting in 20 stitches

c. A turnover of the puck, leading directly to an Oilers goal by Jari Kurri that eliminated the Flames from the playoffs

d. A cross-check to the head of Paul Kariya during a goal celebration, knocking Kariya out of the upcoming Olympics

9. During his 11 years on the Calgary blue line, how many times did Robyn Regehr go an entire season without scoring a single goal?

a. 0

b. 2

c. 5

d. 7

10. Calgary defender Jamie Macoun was involved in several high-profile, violent incidents with opponents. In which of the following was Macoun the victim rather than the aggressor?

    a. A sucker-punching incident with Mark Messier involving a broken cheekbone and a 10-game suspension

    b. A high-sticking incident with Pat Lafontaine involving a broken jaw and dislodged teeth, but no suspension

    c. A hit from behind with Pavel Bure involving a concussion and a four-game suspension

    d. A cross-checking incident with Dale Hawerchuk involving a broken rib but no suspension

11. Defenseman Jay Bouwmeester was an ironman during his time in the NHL. While skating with the Calgary Flames in 2011, he set the NHL record for most consecutive games played by a defenseman by playing in his 486th in a row. How many games did his streak reach before it was stopped?

    a. 487

    b. 650

    c. 737

    d. 1,081

12. Flames defender Phil Housley has played the most NHL games of any player who has never won the Stanley Cup.

    a. True

    b. False

13. Flames mainstay Robyn Regehr played 826 NHL games with the club. Where does he rank in games played all-time for Calgary?

    a. 1st
    b. 2nd
    c. 3rd
    d. 8th

14. Which current Flames defenseman has the longest tenure in Calgary?

    a. Travis Hamonic
    b. Oliver Kylington
    c. T.J. Brodie
    d. Mark Giordano

15. Who holds the Calgary record for most goals by a rookie defenseman, with 20, only the third NHL player to reach that total?

    a. Gary Suter
    b. Al MacInnis
    c. Dion Phaneuf
    d. Dennis Wideman

16. Calgary defenseman Al MacInnis once split a goaltender's mask with a slapshot he fired from outside the offensive zone.

    a. True
    b. False

17. Which of the following facts about Flames defender Robyn Regehr is NOT true?

   a. He broke both legs in a car accident and returned to become the youngest-ever winner of the Bill Masterton Trophy.
   b. He was raised as a young child in a country not known as a hockey hotbed, Indonesia.
   c. He has donated over $15 million to various charities in Calgary.
   d. His brother Richie also played for the Flames.

18. Calgary blue-liner Al MacInnis was named the third greatest athlete (behind Sidney Crosby and curler Colleen Jones) to come from where?

   a. Canada
   b. Scotland
   c. The foster care system
   d. Nova Scotia

19. Former Calgary Flame Dion Phaneuf is married to which celebrity actress?

   a. Megan Fox
   b. Claire Danes
   c. Elisha Cuthbert
   d. Rose McGowan

20. Many players wait until their hockey careers are over to find other work, but Flames defenseman Jamie Macoun ran a toy business and worked in real estate while still playing in the NHL.

a. True

b. False

QUIZ ANSWERS

1. B – Al MacInnis

2. B – False

3. C – Cross-checking a referee from behind and causing a concussion

4. C – As a tribute to his sister, who passed away in a car accident when he was a teenager.

5. B – Paul Reinhart

6. A – Mark Giordano

7. A – True

8. D – A cross-check to the head of Paul Kariya during a goal celebration, knocking Kariya out of the upcoming Olympics

9. B – 2

10. A – A sucker-punching incident with Mark Messier involving a broken cheekbone and a 10-game suspension

11. C – 737

12. B – False

13. C – 3rd

14. D – Mark Giordano

15. C – Dion Phaneuf

16. A – True

17. C – He has donated over $15 million to various charities in Calgary.

18. D – Nova Scotia

19. C – Elisha Cuthbert

20. A – True

DID YOU KNOW?

1. Just two men born in Brazil have ever played in the NHL. Goalie Mike Greenlay was the first, but he started just two games for the Edmonton Oilers in 1990 before disappearing from the league. Calgary had much better success with defenseman Robyn Regehr, who was a beloved presence with the Flames and lasted for 1,089 NHL games.

2. The Flames got a bit lucky in finding Jamie Macoun for their blue line. Macoun was a standout at Ohio State University but was declared ineligible for their team because he had missed a class. Macoun dropped out, the Flames signed him as a free agent, and he promptly made the All-Rookie Team.

3. In 2002, a slapshot from Columbus Blue Jacket Espen Knutsen deflected off Flames defenseman Derek Morris, left the rink, and hit a teenage girl in the head. The girl, Brittanie Cecil, passed away. The incident left Morris shaken and caused the NHL to install safety netting in all rinks the following year.

4. Along with fellow Finns Jarkko Ruutu and Sami Salo, Calgary defenseman Toni Lydman is one of just three members of the "Quadruple Silver Club." This distinction stems from Lydman's losses in the World Championship Final, World Cup Final, Olympic Final, and Stanley Cup Final (achieved with the Flames in 2004).

5. Flames defender Al MacInnis was feared league-wide for his heavy slapshot from the point. MacInnis won the NHL's hardest shot competition more often than anyone else, taking home the title seven times in his career. His shot in the competition topped out at 100.4 miles per hour.

6. After Calgary blue-liner Phil Housley's illustrious career ended, he retired as the NHL's all-time leading scorer among American players, and also as the American with the most NHL games played. His records have since been broken by Mike Modano and Chris Chelios, respectively, but Housley was inducted into both the United States Hockey Hall of Fame and the Hockey Hall of Fame.

7. When Calgary defenseman Dion Phaneuf was just 22 years old and skating in his second season with the Flames, ESPN surveyed NHL players and 43% of respondents already felt that Phaneuf delivered the hardest hits in hockey.

8. Calgary's Gary Suter played over 1,100 NHL games, won a Stanley Cup, and was a five-time All-Star, but he may never have had a single moment as incredible as his older brother Bob Suter, who did not play a single NHL game. Bob was a defenseman for the U.S. Olympic team, who won a gold medal as a member of the famous "Miracle on Ice" team in 1980.

9. Denis Gauthier, who patrolled the blue line for several seasons in Calgary, came by his tough, physical play honestly. His father was a professional wrestler, as were

his uncles, who formed the popular WWF tag team champions, "The Rougeau Brothers."

10. Only one Calgary Flames defender has ever been the recipient of the ESPN Muhammad Ali Sports Humanitarian Award. Team leader Mark Giordano was the honored winner in 2017. He was recognized for his exceptional charity work in helping Calgary schools with physical education equipment, technological upgrades, and personal mentorship.

CHAPTER 10:

CENTERS OF ATTENTION

QUIZ TIME!

1. In five consecutive NHL seasons, center Marc Savard averaged more than a point per game. How many of those seasons came while he was with the Flames?

    a. 0

    b. 1

    c. 2

    d. 5

2. Flames center Sam Bennett scored his first NHL point on his first NHL shift, just 33 seconds into his first NHL game.

    a. True

    b. False

3. Which two childhood best friends eventually became NHL teammates on the Calgary Flames?

    a. Center Sean Monahan and left winger Johnny Gaudreau

b. Center Joe Nieuwendyk and left winger Gary Roberts

c. Centers Curtis Glencross and Daymond Langkow

d. Center Stéphane Yelle and left winger Alex Tanguay

4. Flames center Stéphane Yelle arrived in Calgary in a trade from Colorado and provided extra value for the team by doing what?

a. Becoming an ace in shootouts and leading the team in shootout percentage

b. Serving as the team's chaplain for religious services

c. Filling in on the blue line whenever a defenseman was hurt

d. Insisting on driving the team bus to games in nearby NHL cities

5. When Flames center Doug Risebrough tore off Oilers enforcer Marty McSorley's jersey during a fight, what did Risebrough do with the jersey afterward?

a. Autographed it with his own name and auctioned it off for charity

b. Turned it into a dartboard target in the Flames' locker room

c. Shredded it to pieces with his skate blades

d. Displayed it with a patch reading "Mc-Sore-Loser" over the regular nameplate

6. Which Calgary pivot scored the team's only Stanley Cup-winning goal in franchise history, against the Montreal Canadiens in 1989?

a. Doug Gilmour

b. Joel Otto

    c. Lanny McDonald

    d. Joe Nieuwendyk

7. Flames center Matthew Lombardi once played goaltender for the team during an emergency situation after both Miikka Kiprusoff and Curtis McElhinney were hurt during a game.

    a. True

    b. False

8. Which Flames center was known for dominating the faceoff circle and for his defensive play against top opposing forwards?

    a. Olli Jokinen

    b. Joel Otto

    c. Mikael Backlund

    d. Matt Stajan

9. Flames pivot Curtis Glencross participated as a team member in which sport during the summer after hockey had finished?

    a. Slow-pitch softball

    b. Skeet shooting

    c. Water polo

    d. Chuckwagon racing

10. Which center was born in Toronto, drafted by Toronto, and played in Toronto, yet still loved Calgary so much that he re-signed with the Flames as a free agent after playing just 27 games there and settled in the city with his family after his NHL retirement?

a. Doug Gilmour
b. Tom Lysiak
c. Matt Stajan
d. Jeff Shantz

11. Which Flames center recorded a hat trick at just 19 years old, setting the Calgary record for youngest player to net three goals in a game?

a. Joe Nieuwendyk
b. Sean Monahan
c. Mark Jankowski
d. Sam Bennett

12. There is a song written by a Canadian band about Flames center Joel Otto titled "Two Minutes for Looking So Good."

a. True
b. False

13. Which two Flames linemates played their 1,000th NHL games one after the other on back-to-back nights?

a. Center Joe Nieuwendyk and left winger Gary Roberts
b. Center Mikael Backlund and left winger Michael Frolík
c. Center Daymond Langkow and right winger Jarome Iginla
d. Center Sean Monahan and left winger Johnny Gaudreau

14. Which former Flames center loved golf enough to make a career of it post-hockey, playing on the Celebrity Tour,

winning several tournaments, and caddying for golf legends John Daly and Ernie Els?

    a. Curtis Glencross

    b. Robert Reichel

    c. Lance Bouma

    d. Dan Quinn

15. Which Flames center was the youngest Swedish player ever to score an NHL goal?

    a. Mikael Backlund

    b. Elias Lindholm

    c. Kent Nilsson

    d. Håkan Loob

16. No less an authority than Wayne Gretzky once remarked of Flames center Kent Nilsson: "Skills-wise, he might have been the most skilled hockey player I ever saw in my entire career."

    a. True

    b. False

17. For which sport has former Flame Bill Clement NOT provided play-by-play commentary on television?

    a. Pentathlon

    b. Badminton

    c. Table tennis

    d. Roller hockey

18. Flames center Joel Otto and Oilers superstar Mark Messier were renowned for their battles throughout the 1980s.

Which of the following is NOT an actual remark from Messier about Otto?

    a. "I respected him."

    b. "I sure wish that jerk was on our team!"

    c. "Did I like him? I'm sure he's a wonderful man, but..."

    d. "I owe him my career, in a way."

19. One Flames center was actually named after another Hall of Fame center from an earlier era. Which one was it?

    a. Mark Jankowski, named after Mark Messier

    b. Elias Lindholm, named after Patrik Elias

    c. Joe Nieuwendyk, named after Joe Malone

    d. Clarke Wilm, named after Bobby Clarke

20. Calgary's Jiri Hudler holds the NHL record for the fastest pair of short-handed goals, scoring two just eight seconds apart against the Winnipeg Jets in 2015.

    a. True

    b. False

QUIZ ANSWERS

1. A – 0

2. A – True

3. B – Center Joe Nieuwendyk and left winger Gary Roberts

4. C – Filling in on the blue line whenever a defenseman was hurt

5. C – Shredded it to pieces with his skate blades

6. A – Doug Gilmour

7. B – False

8. B – Joel Otto

9. D – Chuckwagon racing

10. C – Matt Stajan

11. D – Sam Bennett

12. A – True

13. C – Center Daymond Langkow and right winger Jarome Iginla

14. D – Dan Quinn

15. B – Elias Lindholm

16. A – True

17. D – Roller hockey

18. B – "I sure wish that jerk was on our team!"

19. D – Clarke Wilm, named after Bobby Clarke

20. B – False

DID YOU KNOW?

1. Because of his small size, Flames Hall-of-Famer Doug Gilmour went undrafted when he was first eligible for the NHL Draft. He returned to his junior team (Cornwall Royals) and developed his game there, eventually recording a point in 55 consecutive games, which is still an OHL record.

2. Calgary pivot Joe Nieuwendyk had quite the night on January 11, 1989. Nieuwendyk scored five goals in a game against the Winnipeg Jets, setting a team record that has stood for three decades and has been equaled by just 45 other players in NHL history.

3. Bill Clement is likely known more for his post-Flames career than for anything he accomplished on the ice. Clement worked as a broadcaster for ESPN, SportsNet, TNT, ABC, NBC, Versus, Comcast, Sirius XM, CTV, and CBC; provided the voice for EA Sports' NHL game series for several years; and has appeared in over 300 commercial advertisements before founding his own speaking website.

4. Flames center Mikael Backlund is popular both on the ice and in the community. For several years, he has donated $150 for each point he scores to Kid's Cancer Care Foundation in Calgary, and $200 per point to the ALS Society of Alberta.

5. Among many Flames who decided to take less money to remain in Calgary was free-agent center Curtis Glencross in 2011. He liked the fact that it was close to his home province of Saskatchewan and thought playing with Jarome Iginla would help his game. He was correct, as he led the NHL with a shooting percentage of 23.6% the following season.

6. Center Sean Monahan was such a mature youngster and polished player that the Flames kept him on their NHL roster as an 18-year-old directly after his draft year. Monahan rewarded their faith, becoming the sixth-youngest player ever to score 100 career goals, behind only notable stars Alexander Ovechkin, Patrick Kane, Sidney Crosby, Steven Stamkos, and Jaromir Jagr.

7. Flames center Carey Wilson is a multitalented man. In addition to suiting up for Calgary, he also obtained a medical degree from the Ivy League's Dartmouth College. Incredibly, his father Jerry Wilson also played in the NHL and became a doctor as well.

8. Calgary center Joe Nieuwendyk is one of just 11 players in NHL history to win a Stanley Cup with three teams. Nieuwendyk helped Calgary win in 1989, led Dallas to victory a decade later, then secured his third with New Jersey in 2003.

9. Jeff Shantz, who played for the Flames during the late 1990s and early 2000s, is the nephew of Joseph Martin, who was the Dean of Harvard Medical School.

10. Poor Olli Jokinen played 1,231 regular-season games in the NHL (including 236 for the Flames). During stints with the Kings, Islanders, Rangers, Flames, Panthers, Coyotes, Jets, Predators, Maple Leafs, and Blues, Jokinen only ever made the playoffs once, playing just six playoff games in Calgary in 2009.

CHAPTER 11:

THE WINGERS TAKE FLIGHT

QUIZ TIME!

1. Which of the following facts about Flames winger Theoren Fleury is NOT true?

    a. He launched his own clothing line, called "FAKE."
    b. He purchased the Calgary Hitmen hockey team with Joe Sakic and Bret Hart.
    c. He recorded and released a country music album called *I Am Who I Am*.
    d. He ran his own small business as a taxi and limousine driver.

2. Calgary icon Jarome Iginla's full name is Jarome Arthur-Leigh Adekunle Tig Junior Elvis Iginla.

    a. True
    b. False

3. Which Calgary winger set the NHL record for most consecutive goals scored without a single one coming on the power play (124)?

a. Håkan Loob

b. Jim Peplinski

c. Valeri Bure

d. Kristian Huselius

4. After his retirement, Jarome Iginla purchased his junior hockey team, the Kamloops Blazers, along with three other NHL players. Which one was NOT part of that ownership group?

   a. Mark Recchi

   b. Darryl Sydor

   c. Daymond Langkow

   d. Shane Doan

5. Which Flames winger was a physical fitness fanatic during his playing career, and then became a personal trainer with his own high-performance center and fitness institute after his retirement?

   a. Gary Roberts

   b. Tim Hunter

   c. Dave Lowry

   d. Ron Stern

6. How did right winger Theoren Fleury celebrate a big goal against the Edmonton Oilers after a Mark Messier giveaway in their 1991 playoff series?

   a. Firing a pretend bow and arrow at the Oilers' Stanley Cup banner hanging in the rafters

   b. Skating in front of the Oilers' bench, staring at them for about 10 seconds, then saluting

c. Skating directly into the tunnel and immediately leaving the ice for the dressing room

d. Sliding on his knees across most of the rink's ice surface before being dogpiled by his teammates

7. Flames right winger Sergei Makarov was 31 when he won the Calder Trophy, the oldest Rookie of the Year in NHL history.

   a. True
   b. False

8. About which forward did Calgary's general manager remark, upon acquiring the player: "He's the Wayne Gretzky of Sweden."?

   a. Kent Nilsson
   b. Mikael Backlund
   c. Håkan Loob
   d. Elias Lindholm

9. Which of the following facts about Flames star Lanny McDonald is NOT true?

   a. He was well-known and easily recognized by his iconic bushy red mustache.
   b. The song "Old McDonald Had a Farm" was written about his father, a farmer in Alberta.
   c. His middle name is King, after Toronto Maple Leafs star King Clancy.
   d. He became chairman of the board for the Hockey Hall of Fame after his retirement.

10. During the Flames' Stanley Cup run in the 1989 NHL playoffs, which winger led the team in goals with 16?

    a. Joe Mullen
    b. Håkan Loob
    c. Sergei Makarov
    d. Gary Roberts

11. Flames winger Alex Tanguay led the NHL in what special skill during the 2010-11 season?

    a. Faceoff percentage
    b. Shootout goals
    c. Short-handed goals
    d. Penalties drawn

12. Winger Valeri Bure participated in a figure skating competition show called *Battle of the Blades*. He and his partner, skater Ekaterina Gordeeva, won first place on the show.

    a. True
    b. False

13. Star winger Jarome Iginla led all NHL rookies in points during his first year with Calgary, but lost the Calder Trophy to which player?

    a. Ottawa Senator Daniel Alfredsson
    b. Boston Bruin Sergei Samsonov
    c. Colorado Avalanche Chris Drury
    d. New York Islander Bryan Berard

14. Which Flames winger courageously spoke up about his childhood sexual abuse by his hockey coach in a best-selling book called *Playing with Fire*?

    a. Sheldon Kennedy
    b. Andrew Mangiapane
    c. Theoren Fleury
    d. Sandy McCarthy

15. Which winger scored the first-ever goal for the Flames in the Olympic Saddledome?

    a. Eric Vail
    b. Lanny McDonald
    c. Eddy Beers
    d. Larry Romanchych

16. Right winger Jarome Iginla was such a good athlete that he spent time as the catcher for the Canadian National Junior Team.

    a. True
    b. False

17. What led to Calgary icon Theoren Fleury's retirement from the NHL in 2003?

    a. A desire to travel less and spend more time with his family
    b. A concussion that knocked him out of action toward the end of the season
    c. Drug and alcohol addiction that he struggled to overcome

d. A disagreement about contract terms that left him unwilling to play

18. Which Flames power forward was the first NHL player to score 50 goals and accumulate 200 penalty minutes in the same season?

    a. Jarome Iginla
    b. Theoren Fleury
    c. Gary Roberts
    d. Matthew Tkachuk

19. Current Flames winger Matthew Tkachuk has an ongoing feud that is well covered by the media with which opposing defenseman?

    a. Brent Burns of the San Jose Sharks
    b. Darnell Nurse of the Edmonton Oilers
    c. Oliver Ekman-Larsson of the Arizona Coyotes
    d. Drew Doughty of the Los Angeles Kings

20. Lanny McDonald once shaved his walrus-style mustache in a commercial for which Gillette paid him $500,000 to endorse their razors.

    a. True
    b. False

QUIZ ANSWERS

1. D – He ran his own small business as a taxi and limousine driver.

2. A – True

3. B – Jim Peplinski

4. C – Daymond Langkow

5. A – Gary Roberts

6. D – Sliding on his knees across most of the rink's ice surface before being dogpiled by his teammates

7. A – True

8. C – Håkan Loob

9. B – The song "Old McDonald Had a Farm" was written about his father, a farmer in Alberta.

10. A – Joe Mullen

11. B – Shootout goals

12. A – True

13. D – New York Islander Bryan Berard

14. C – Theoren Fleury

15. B – Lanny McDonald

16. A – True

17. C – Drug and alcohol addiction that he struggled to overcome

18. C – Gary Roberts

19. D – Drew Doughty of the Los Angeles Kings

20. B – False

DID YOU KNOW?

1. Flames right winger Jarome Iginla is only the second black NHL player inducted into the Hall of Fame. Iginla followed goaltender Grant Fuhr, who also briefly played for the Flames.

2. Talented winger Theoren Fleury had many doubters because of his short 5'6" stature. But Fleury proved them all wrong, recording over a point per game for over 1,000 NHL games. Fleury did not shrink from physical play, either, and racked up over 1,800 career penalty minutes.

3. Not only did right winger Valeri Bure lead the Calgary Flames with 35 goals in 1999-2000; his brother Pavel Bure led the Florida Panthers with 58. Their combined total of 93 was the highest ever achieved by brothers in a single NHL season.

4. Calgary winger Jarome Iginla won five gold medals during his career. He started with the World Junior Championship, notched the World Championship, added an Olympic gold medal, then a World Cup, and finally added another Olympic gold medal for good measure. Sadly, he never managed to capture a Stanley Cup.

5. During gym class at Chaminade College Preparatory School, Flames winger Matthew Tkachuk competed against future star Boston Celtics forward Jayson Tatum.

6. Calgary Flames forward Eddy Beers is one of just four

NHL players to have been born in the Netherlands. Beers ranks third in games played among them but is the top Dutch scorer in both goals and points.

7. During the 2001-02 season, Flames star Jarome Iginla led the league in goals and points. He finished tied with Montreal goalie Jose Theodore for the league's MVP award, but it went to Theodore because the goalie had more first-place votes. Controversy ensued when it was discovered that a voter, believed to be from Quebec, had left Iginla off his ballot entirely, and the NHL changed its voting rules afterward.

8. Physical fan-favorite Micheal Ferland was once arrested and charged with aggravated assault after an off-season bar fight. At his trial two years later, Ferland was found not guilty after the jury determined he had simply defended himself against an intoxicated Edmonton Oilers fan who had sucker-punched him.

9. U.S.-born winger Joe Mullen did not learn to skate until he was ten years old, but he still managed to win a Stanley Cup with the Calgary Flames (and two more with the Pittsburgh Penguins), and he was also elected to the Hockey Hall of Fame.

10. April 11, 2014, was a big day in the life of winger Johnny Gaudreau. Not only did he receive the Hobey Baker Award as the best hockey player in the NCAA, but he also made his NHL debut with the Calgary Flames. Gaudreau was instantly electric, scoring a goal on his very first shot.

CHAPTER 12:

COACHES, GMS, & OWNERS

QUIZ TIME!

1. Who was the Flames' first general manager?

   a. Jay Feaster

   b. Doug Risebrough

   c. Craig Button

   d. Cliff Fletcher

2. Brent Sutter was hired as Flames head coach three years after brother Darryl Sutter, who was hired as Flames head coach three years after brother Brian Sutter.

   a. True

   b. False

3. The Flames' first head coach, Al MacNeil, lasted for how long in that position with the franchise?

   a. 36 games

   b. 1 season

   c. 2 seasons

   d. 8 seasons

4. Which of the following familial facts about Flames leaders is NOT true?

   a. Coach Jim Playfair has a son who stars on the TV series *Letterkenny*.
   b. GM Brad Treliving has a father who starred on the TV series *Dragon's Den*.
   c. GM Craig Button starred on the TV show *NHL on the Fly*.
   d. Coach Glen Gulutzan has a daughter who starred in the movie *The Dark Knight Rises*.

5. Which deceased Flames leader is best remembered for his catchphrase, "It's a great day for hockey."?

   a. Coach Mike Keenan
   b. GM Brian Burke
   c. Coach Bob Johnson
   d. GM Al Coates

6. Flames general manager Cliff Fletcher was one of the first to dip heavily into the U.S. college system to find good players. Which of the following skaters did he NOT sign from this system?

   a. Colin Patterson
   b. Joel Otto
   c. Doug Gilmour
   d. Gary Suter

7. Flames head coach Bill Peters resigned from his position with the team after allegations of racist behavior in his past.

a. True

b. False

8. Which Calgary general manager once skated as a player on the team before getting the chance to guide it from the front office?

    a. Doug Risebrough

    b. Brian Sutter

    c. Brian Burke

    d. Brad Treliving

9. Which coach led the Calgary Flames to their sole Stanley Cup championship?

    a. Bob Johnson

    b. Mike Keenan

    c. Bob Hartley

    d. Terry Crisp

10. How many of the Flames' 18 head coaches have spent their entire NHL coaching career with Calgary?

    a. 0

    b. 2

    c. 5

    d. 8

11. Who is the Flames' leader in all-time regular-season coaching wins with the franchise?

    a. Bob Johnson

    b. Terry Crisp

    c. Brent Sutter

    d. Bob Hartley

12. Calgary is the only NHL franchise to have a player rise from skating for the team to ownership of the team.

    a. True
    b. False

13. Which head coach stirred up controversy when he stepped down as coach of the New Jersey Devils for family reasons, only to sign on as the Flames' head coach just two weeks later?

    a. Terry Crisp
    b. Pierre Page
    c. Mike Keenan
    d. Brent Sutter

14. Calgary general manager Cliff "Silver Fox" Fletcher was also known by which other nickname?

    a. "Fixated Fletcher" because of his focus on the defense position above all others.
    b. "The No Deal Cowboy" because he refused to listen to offers for the team's best players.
    c. "Papa Cliffy" because players thought he looked after them like a father.
    d. "Trader Cliff" because of his penchant for making deals with other teams.

15. Which Flames general manager has led the franchise to the most playoff appearances?

    a. Al Coates
    b. Cliff Fletcher

c. Brad Treliving

d. Craig Button

16. Flames owner Ken King once proposed trading franchises with Edmonton Oilers owner Peter Pocklington as part of a business deal.

   a. True

   b. False

17. Which Flames general manager had a father who worked for the Rochester Americans and a mother who worked for the Toronto Maple Leafs?

   a. Al Coates

   b. Brian Burke

   c. Brad Treliving

   d. Craig Button

18. How many owners were part of the initial purchase of the Atlanta Flames franchise in 1980?

   a. 1

   b. 2

   c. 4

   d. 7

19. Which Flames coach is the only one to have won the Jack Adams Award as the league's top coach while behind the bench for Calgary?

   a. Bob Johnson

   b. Terry Crisp

   c. Darryl Sutter

   d. Bob Hartley

20. While serving as general manager of the Calgary Flames, Cliff Fletcher was the first GM in the NHL to use a Russian player (Sergei Priakin in 1988).

    a. True
    b. False

QUIZ ANSWERS

1. D – Cliff Fletcher

2. A – True

3. C – 2 seasons

4. D – Coach Glen Gulutzan has a daughter who starred in the movie *The Dark Knight Rises.*

5. C – Coach Bob Johnson

6. C – Doug Gilmour

7. A – True

8. A – Doug Risebrough

9. D – Terry Crisp

10. C – 5

11. A – Bob Johnson

12. B – False

13. D – Brent Sutter

14. D – "Trader Cliff" because of his penchant for making deals with other teams.

15. B – Cliff Fletcher

16. B – False

17. D – Craig Button

18. D – 7

19. D – Bob Hartley

20. A – True

DID YOU KNOW?

1. Calgary coach and general manager Darryl Sutter runs a 3,000-acre beef cattle farm in Alberta. Before taking the Flames' jobs, he was injured in a fall on the farm and suffered injuries worse than many of those he'd received playing hockey, a fractured skull and a broken shoulder blade.

2. Of the Flames' initial owners in Calgary, five were in the oil business. The sixth, Norman Kwong, starred for the Calgary Stampeders and was the first-ever player of Chinese descent in the CFL as well as the first to make it into the Hall of Fame. He later became the first person of Chinese heritage to serve as lieutenant governor of Alberta.

3. Popular NHL commentator Brian Burke once held a position with the Flames that existed for only two other NHL clubs: president of hockey operations. During his tenure in this role, he fired Jay Feaster as Calgary's general manager and hired current GM Brad Treliving.

4. Calgary Sports and Entertainment Corporation, the current owners of the Flames, also owns and operates the Calgary Roughnecks of the NLL, Calgary Stampeders of the CFL, Calgary Hitmen of the WHL, and Stockton Heat of the AHL.

5. The team's very first coach, back when they were still the

Atlanta Flames, was Hockey Hall-of-Famer Bernie Geoffrion. Geoffrion had to leave his position for health reasons and ended up as a broadcaster for the team instead, but never made it to Calgary with them.

6. Only two men have served as both coach and general manager of the Calgary Flames. Darryl Sutter was one of these men. Sutter coached the team to a 107-73-15 record and led them on a trip to the Stanley Cup Finals, but resigned the coaching gig shortly afterward because he felt that it was too difficult for one man to do both jobs well.

7. The other coach/general manager in Calgary's history was Doug Risebrough, who did just about everything he could for the organization. Risebrough also held positions with the team as a player, assistant coach, and assistant GM.

8. Before becoming general manager of the Flames, Jay Feaster held the same position with the Tampa Bay Lightning. Feaster and the Lightning beat the Flames in the 2003-04 Stanley Cup Finals, and Calgary remembered the job he did with that team all too well when they hired him years later.

9. The idea for an NHL General Manager of the Year Trophy was first proposed by Brian Burke in 1993 before the trophy was created in 2010. While Burke did work briefly as the Flames' GM, neither he nor anyone else in Calgary has won the award he spearheaded.

10. Of the seven Sutter brothers, five worked for the Flames at some point in their careers. Brian Sutter coached the team

from 1997 to 2000. Darryl Sutter was both coach and general manager and was employed in Calgary from 2002 to 2010. Brent Sutter was hired as head coach after Darryl focused on just the general manager aspect. Ron Sutter both played for the team and then joined their scouting staff after his retirement. Finally, Duane Sutter served as the team's director of player personnel.

CHAPTER 13:

THE AWARDS SECTION

QUIZ TIME!

1. Which Flame has been selected as an NHL First or Second Team All-Star most often while with Calgary?

    a. Miikka Kiprusoff
    b. Mike Vernon
    c. Jarome Iginla
    d. Al MacInnis

2. The first Flame to win any major award given out by the NHL after the team moved to Calgary was franchise winger Lanny McDonald.

    a. True
    b. False

3. During which season did the Flames win their first Presidents' Trophy for leading the NHL in points?

    a. 1986-87
    b. 1987-88
    c. 1988-89
    d. 1991-92

4. The NHL's Plus-Minus Award for best plus/minus total during a season has been won by three Flames. Which of the following did NOT win this award?

    a. Brad McCrimmon
    b. Theoren Fleury
    c. Gary Suter
    d. Joe Mullen

5. How many goals did Jarome Iginla score in 2001-02 and 2003-04 to take home the Maurice "Rocket" Richard Trophy for most goals in the NHL?

    a. 48 and 60
    b. 52 and 41
    c. 45 and 49
    d. 50 and 50

6. Since 2006, the NHL has given out the Mark Messier Leadership Award. Which Flame has been honored as its winner?

    a. Craig Conroy
    b. Theoren Fleury
    c. Mark Giordano
    d. Jarome Iginla

7. There is a special prize given out to the top Finnish player in the NHL each year, called the Sauna Award. Goaltender Miikka Kiprusoff has won the award twice while tending the net for Calgary.

    a. True
    b. False

8. Who was the most recent Calgary player to make the NHL All-Rookie Team?

    a. Johnny Gaudreau
    b. Matthew Tkachuk
    c. Dion Phaneuf
    d. Håkan Loob

9. Which Flames goaltender won the franchise's first-ever William M. Jennings Trophy for allowing the fewest goals in a season?

    a. Mike Vernon
    b. Miikka Kiprusoff
    c. David Rittich
    d. Fred Brathwaite

10. Which of these Flames icons is the only one to win an Art Ross Trophy as the league's leading scorer?

    a. Joe Nieuwendyk
    b. Theoren Fleury
    c. Johnny Gaudreau
    d. Jarome Iginla

11. The Lady Byng Memorial Trophy for sportsmanship, gentlemanly conduct, and playing ability has been won by three players in Calgary's franchise history. Which player won it twice with the Flames?

    a. Jiri Hudler
    b. Johnny Gaudreau
    c. Joe Mullen
    d. Craig Conroy

12. There is a special prize given out to the top Swedish player in the NHL each year, called the Viking Award. Forwards Kent Nilsson and Håkan Loob have won this award while skating for the Flames.

    a. True
    b. False

13. Which of the following Flames players won the Calder Memorial Trophy as the league's top rookie?

    a. Gary Suter, Joe Nieuwendyk, and Sergei Makarov
    b. Kent Nilsson, Sergei Makarov, Theoren Fleury, and Dion Phaneuf
    c. Gary Roberts, Jarome Iginla, and Johnny Gaudreau
    d. Al MacInnis, Miikka Kiprusoff, Sean Monahan, and Matthew Tkachuk

14. Of the Flames in the Hockey Hall of Fame, Al MacInnis and Lanny McDonald are the first among them to skate with Calgary. What year did they begin playing with the team?

    a. 1980
    b. 1981
    c. 1984
    d. 1986

15. Which Flames player has been selected for the most NHL All-Star Games while with Calgary?

    a. Al MacInnis
    b. Theoren Fleury

c. Mike Vernon

d. Jarome Iginla

16. Flames broadcaster Peter Maher has been recognized for his years of excellence doing radio calls for Calgary with the Foster Hewitt Memorial Award.

    a. True

    b. False

17. The James Norris Trophy, given annually to the NHL's best defenseman, has been won by how many Calgary Flames players?

    a. None

    b. 1 – Mark Giordano

    c. 2 – Al MacInnis and Mark Giordano

    d. 4 – Al MacInnis, Gary Suter, Phil Housley, and Mark Giordano

18. How many Calgary Flames have been elected to the Hall of Fame in the builders category?

    a. 0

    b. 2

    c. 5

    d. 11

19. In which year did Calgary host the NHL's annual All-Star Game?

    a. 1980

    b. 1985

    c. 1998

    d. 2007

20. During the early 1990s, the NHL held a "Toughman Competition" during the off-season which featured players competing in feats of strength for a cash prize. Flames forward Gary Roberts won the competition twice.

   a. True
   b. False

QUIZ ANSWERS

1. D – Al MacInnis

2. A – True

3. B – 1987-88

4. C – Gary Suter

5. B – 52 and 41

6. D – Jarome Iginla

7. B – False

8. A – Johnny Gaudreau

9. B – Miikka Kiprusoff

10. D – Jarome Iginla

11. C – Joe Mullen

12. A – True

13. A – Gary Suter, Joe Nieuwendyk, and Sergei Makarov

14. B – 1981

15. D – Jarome Iginla

16. A – True

17. B – 1 – Mark Giordano

18. C – 5

19. B – 1985

20. B – False

DID YOU KNOW?

1. The Bill Masterton Trophy, for perseverance, sportsmanship, and dedication to hockey, has been won by two Flames, 13 years apart. Lanny McDonald got the trophy first, in 1982-83, for his dedication to the game. In 1995-96, Gary Roberts came back from career-threatening bone spurs and nerve damage, which garnered him the prestigious award as well.

2. The NHL Man of the Year Award existed for only four seasons, but a Flame won it during that short span. Lanny McDonald was given the award in 1988-89. Eventually, the NHL switched to a similar award called the NHL Foundation Player Award, which existed for nearly two decades. Both Jarome Iginla and Mark Giordano nabbed that award while with the Flames, as well.

3. Only one Flame has ever taken home the Vezina Trophy as the NHL's best goaltender. That was Miikka Kiprusoff in 2005-06, when he posted the best full-season numbers of his career: a 2.07 goals-against average and a .923 save percentage.

4. Eleven players who skated with Calgary have been elected to the Hockey Hall of Fame. Some, such as Grant Fuhr, Phil Housley, Brett Hull, and Martin St. Louis, clearly made their biggest marks in the game elsewhere, but Doug Gilmour, Jarome Iginla, Al MacInnis, Sergei Makarov,

Lanny McDonald, Joe Mullen, and Joe Nieuwendyk meant a lot to the city and contributed significantly to Flames' history.

5. The Flames have never had a player win the Frank J. Selke Trophy as the NHL's best defensive forward. Center Doug Gilmour had received votes for the award but did not win it until 1992-93, the year after he was traded to the Toronto Maple Leafs.

6. Calgary's lone Stanley Cup championship ties them in the all-time rankings with several other teams: the Ducks, Capitals, Blues, Lightning, Stars, and Hurricanes. That's still ahead of the 11 teams who have never won it!

7. Since their inaugural season in Calgary, the Flames have awarded the 3-Star Cup at the end of the season, given to the player who has received the most "3-star selections" during the year. Jarome Iginla won this cup six times while with the Flames, and he remains the club leader.

8. One Calgary Flame has won the Ted Lindsay Award for the NHL's Most Valuable Player, as voted by other players. Winger Jarome Iginla was recognized in 2001-02, the same year in which he controversially lost the Hart Trophy to Montreal goaltender Jose Theodore.

9. The Lester Patrick Trophy is awarded each year for outstanding service to hockey in the United States. Three men connected to the Flames have won this trophy: coach Bob Johnson, defenseman Phil Housley, and forward Joe Mullen.

10. Flames forward Jim Peplinski was the last-ever winner of the NHL's Charlie Conacher Humanitarian Award before it was discontinued in 1984. Peplinski was very active in the community and worked especially closely with Big Brothers and the Special Olympics.

CONCLUSION

There you have it; an amazing collection of Flames trivia, information, and statistics at your fingertips! Regardless of how you fared on the quizzes, we hope that you found this book entertaining, enlightening, and educational.

Ideally, you knew many of these details but also learned a good deal more about the history of the Calgary Flames, their players, coaches, management, and some of the quirky stories surrounding the team. If you got a little peek into the colorful details that make being a fan so much more enjoyable, then mission accomplished!

The good news is, the trivia doesn't have to stop there! Spread the word. Challenge your fellow Flames fans to see if they can do any better. Share some of the stories with the next generation to help them become Calgary supporters, too.

If you are a big enough Flames fan, consider creating your own quiz with some of the details you know that weren't presented here and then test your friends to see if they can match your knowledge.

The Calgary Flames are a storied franchise. They have a long history with multiple periods of success (and a few that were less than successful). They've had glorious superstars, iconic moments, hilarious tales...but, most of all, they have wonderful, passionate fans. Thank you for being one of them.

Manufactured by Amazon.ca
Bolton, ON